C000143414

GREEK MYTHOLOGY

OEDIPUS

Stephanides Brothers'

GREEK MYTHOLOGY

OEDIPUS
THE TRAGEDIES OF THE THEBAN CYCLE

ⳇ

Retold by Menelaos Stephanides
Drawings by Yannis Stephanides

Translation
Bruce Walter

SIGMA

OEDIPUS
THE TRAGEDIES

First edition 1999, 5th run 2013
Printed in Greece by "Fotolio & Typicon", bound by G. Betsoris
© 2013 Dimitris M. Stefanidis

SIGMA PUBLICATIONS
30, Lekanidi Street, Ag. Dimitrios, 173 43 Athens, Greece
Tel.: +30 210 3607667, Fax: +30 210 3638941
www.sigmabooks.gr, e-mail: sbooks@sigmabooks.gr

ISBN: 978-960-425-074-5

TRAGEDY: a strong word, yet one which pales before the greatest human drama of all times – the story of king Oedipus.

CONTENTS

THE BLACK FATE OF OEDIPUS

"Ah, Zeus, you are a tyrant. You have no pity upon Man. First you create him, then you fill his life with trials and tribulations."

If the great poet Homer uses these harsh words to take the lord of gods and men to task for the sufferings of Odysseus, what words will suffice to tell of the fate the gods reserved for Oedipus, when they cast him into the blackest depths of misery and misfortune?

The destiny of Oedipus was fixed before he even came into the world. His father, Laius, was burdened with a dreadful curse. Welcomed as a guest by Pelops, king of Pisa, he had behaved so vilely towards his handsome son Chrysippus that the young man killed himself for shame. Wild with grief that could not be consoled, his father had cried out:

"Son of Labdacus, it is you who killed my boy, and so I give you both my wish and my curse, too. My wish is that you never bear a son to know the pain of losing him – but if you do, may you be cursed to meet death at your own son's hand!"

Laius paid little heed to Pelops' bitter words. He went back home to Thebes and in time inherited the throne of his father, Labdacus. Yet a day would come when he would pay a heavy price for having abused that hospitality so foully. Not only would he pay in person, but all the clan of Labdacus in their turn, and the innocent Oedipus most dearly of them all.

Years later, Laius married Iocaste, the daughter of Menoeceus. He had no children by her, though, and this weighed heavily with him, for now there would be no one of his line to rule the kingdom after him.

"I shall go to Apollo's oracle at Delphi," he told Iocaste, "to learn what is to blame and beg the god to grant us a son who shall succeed me."

Although Iocaste did not have much faith in oracles, she nodded her agreement, and so, loaded with rich gifts, Laius set out to seek Apollo's aid.

Yet when he heard the prophecy Apollo's priestess had in store for him, Laius quailed in horror.

"Son of Labdacus," intoned the Pythoness, voicing the stern god's words, "you begged to know the joy of fatherhood. You shall have the son that you desire – but your fate shall be to die at the hands of your own child and all your line to drown in their own blood. It is the will of Zeus, the son of Cronus, that the death of Chrysippus may not go unavenged."

With bowed head, Laius made the journey back to Thebes.

"So Pelops' curse was not just bluster, after all," he told himself, and as he rode, he pondered how he might evade his fate. At last he reached the palace, and when he found Iocaste he told her curtly:

"As of tonight, we sleep in separate rooms."

"Why?" asked Iocaste in dismay.

"So that we never have a child."

"You, of all people, now tell me such a thing?" she asked him in bewilderment.

"Yes, I – who longed so dearly for a son. But now, alas, the oracle at Delphi has warned me I shall die at the hands of my own child!"

Iocaste did not share her husband's fears.

"Most oracles prove false," she answered lightly, "and here you are telling me we should not have a child, when we both long for one so desperately?"

Yet Laius' mind was not so easily to be changed, and Iocaste, who still yearned to have a baby, decided to trick her husband. On the next occasion that he held a banquet, she refilled Laius' wine-cup time and time again until the king was drunk. Then she led him to her bedchamber and slept with him in the same bed.

Sure enough, nine months later the child was born whom Laius had been so anxious to avoid. It was a boy. His mother was delighted, but his father, fearing the oracle would prove true, had no thought in his mind but how he might destroy his son. And so, before the child was three days old, he gave it to a faithful herdsman, with orders to take the infant high up on the slopes of Mount Cythaeron and leave it there to be devoured by wild beasts. Fearing the baby might somehow crawl away and be found by kindly people, he drove an iron rod through its feet, bound them with rope, and ordered the herdsman to tie the baby to a tree. Seeing the horror in his servant's eyes, he added:

"Do exactly as I tell you, or I shall tear you apart with my own hands!"

"Your majesty, I shall carry out your orders," replied the

shepherd, but as he left, his ears rang with Iocaste's despairing cries, the grief of a mother losing all a woman holds most precious, be she queen or beggar. Her wailing drove out all thought of abandoning the child to the mercy of the wolves and vultures, and the poor fellow racked his brains to find a way of saving it.

On the hillside he met an old friend of his, another shepherd who was tending the flocks of king Polybus of Corinth. Knowing the man to be a good-hearted fellow, he told him how the infant had been given him by a cruel nobleman, with orders to leave it in the mountains, where the wild beasts would devour it.

"Give the lad to me," the other shepherd offered. "I'll take him down to Corinth and give him to king Polybus. He has no children, and I'm sure he will be glad to take him in."

"On one condition, though," replied king Laius' shepherd. "Never tell anyone it was me who gave the child to you. Say that you found him, tell them any tale you like – but don't reveal it was the king of Thebes' man let you have the boy."

Having agreed on this, the two of them released the poor child's legs and cleaned the bloody wounds as best they could. Then the second shepherd cradled the baby gently in his arms and took him down to king Polybus in Corinth.

Polybus and his wife Merope were delighted by the unexpected gift, and as they had not been blessed with children they decided to bring the boy up as their own, so that one day he might rule over Corinth. Now a name was needed, and looking at the swellings where the poor child's feet had been so cruelly pierced, they decided to call him Oedipus, or 'Swollen-foot'.

Oedipus spent his childhood in the palace of Polybus, believing the king and Merope to be his real parents. With the passing of the years he grew into a fine young man – handsome, strong, clever and brave. Victor in every athletic contest save for running and jumping, he was admired by all his peers. He had one failing: his temper was quick to flare – and in this he was just like Laius, his true father.

Once, at a drinking session, a young noble who had taken more wine than he could hold, started to laugh at Oedipus and make fun of him, forgetting it was the heir to the throne of Corinth that he was addressing. Oedipus answered angrily, insulting the youth in front of everybody present, only to have an even deeper insult flung straight back in his face:

"Bastard! Do you really think Polybus is your father?"

"What did you say, fellow?" roared Oedipus, beside himself with rage – and with a single blow he laid the other senseless on the floor.

Yet from that moment onwards, Oedipus was plagued by doubts. He voiced his fears to Polybus and Merope, who tried to allay them by assuring him he was their real son. But Oedi-

pus could not let the matter rest and decided to go to Delphi
and ask Apollo's oracle. When he came before the Pythoness
to put his question, he was determined to accept whatever
prophecy the god might grant to him, even if it revealed that
he was the son of the humblest beggar.

The answer the god voiced through his priestess' lips was
more horrifying still:

"Leave this place, cursed mortal. You will ascend your
father's throne when you have killed him, then marry your
own mother, and father children on her who will be loathed
by gods and men alike."

Shaken to the core, and believing that the oracle spoke of
Polybus and Merope, Oedipus decided he would not return to
Corinth. Instead he took the road which led to Thebes, the
city where his real father, Laius, lived and ruled.

That very day, Laius himself had set out from Thebes for
Delphi. He was coming to ask the oracle how the Thebans
might be delivered from the Sphinx, a fearsome monster which
was terrorising the city and all the lands about it. Drawn by
his charioteer, Laius was accompanied by his herald and three
serving men. As fate would have it, father and son, who were
strangers to each other, were destined to meet at a crossing of
the ways, where a road led off to nearby Daulis, and in a spot
so narrow there was just room for one chariot to get through.
Not guessing that this was a royal party bearing down on him,

Oedipus did not think to stand aside, sure there was room for the chariot to pass if he kept well to his side of the road.

"Stop where you are, young man!" cried Laius. "First let your betters pass!"

"I have no betters but my parents and the gods!" retorted Oedipus and instead of waiting for the chariot to go first, he tried to make his way past it.

"I'll make pulp of you, you braggart!" screamed the charioteer in fury, and pulled on the reins so that the heavy, iron-bound wheel ran over Oedipus' left foot. At the same moment, Laius lifted high his whip and brought it slashing down across the young man's face. What followed was inevitable: raging with pain, Oedipus struck the king fair and square in the chest with his staff – so hard that Laius toppled lifeless from the chariot. The others fell on him with swords and spears but none had Oedipus's strength and skill, and one by one his attackers met their death. Only one of them had not dared use his weapon, preferring to escape the danger as fast as his legs would carry him.

After the killings at the crossroad, Oedipus continued on his way to Thebes, not guessing he had just slain the ruler of that city, and that this man was his father. As he was crossing Mount Phikion, he caught sight of the Sphinx, perched on a rock beside the road.

The Sphinx was a monster with a woman's head and

... "I'll make pulp of you, you braggart!"...

breasts, the body of a lion, an eagle's wings, iron talons and a tail which ended in a dragon's jaws. This creature was the daughter of Typhoon and Echidne, and the Thebans lived in terror of her. Her claws could tear men and animals to shreds, and many a brave young fellow who had found the courage to challenge her had died in the attempt. Her favourite way of luring victims to destruction was to stop passers-by and give them a knotty riddle to solve. No one could ever answer, and each time, the Sphinx devoured another victim. However, it was said that if anyone could come up with the solution, the Sphinx would throw herself from the rock in furious rage and be dashed to pieces. Just what the riddle was, no one had ever learned, for of all those who had gone to hear it, none had ever returned.

Yet when the fearless Oedipus laid eyes on the Sphinx, he approached her determined to rid Thebes of her pestilential presence or die in the attempt like all the others.

Having caught sight of him, the winged monster showed no sign of wanting to attack. She preferred to humiliate the hero first by setting him a riddle he could never solve.

"What is the creature," she asked him, "which moves in the morning on all fours, walks upright on two legs at noon, and in the evening walks three-legged?"

As soon as Oedipus had heard the riddle, he answered without hesitation: "It is man. In the morning of his life he crawls on hands and knees, and that makes four; when he grows to manhood he walks on two legs; and when he grows old he needs a stick to help him get along, and that makes three."

Before he had even finished speaking, the Sphinx swelled up and shook with rage, so violently that she toppled from her rocky perch and fell with a thunderous crash which shook the countryside for miles around. The fearsome monster was no more. Oedipus, using no other weapon but the power of his mind, had saved Thebes from disaster. Soon, all those who had gone into hiding for fear of the Sphinx emerged and ran to smother Oedipus in their embraces. Then they lifted their new hero shoulder-high and carried him in triumph off to Thebes.

Meanwhile, the survivor of the battle at the crossroads had got back to the city. Hardly daring to reveal his dreadful news, he told how the king and all his other followers had been killed. Ashamed to admit that a single man on foot had defeated them unaided, he made out that a whole gang of robbers had fallen on the royal party.

When the people's grief at the king's death had subsided, Iocaste's brother Creon called all the citizens to a public meeting.

"Men of Thebes," he told them. "Evils fall upon us thick and fast. Not only do we live in terror of the Sphinx, but now we have lost our king, just as he was on his way to Delphi to learn how we might rid ourselves of that vile monster. For days, our state has been ungoverned, for as you know, there is no successor to the throne. A ship without a captain will not sail far, but when the captain has to face a menace like the Sphinx, the ship is just as much at risk, however good he is. I thus propose that we come to a decision which will both save us from the monster and give a new king to our people. Let us announce that whoever succeeds in rescuing Thebes from the clutches of the Sphinx will take the throne of Laius as his prize, and with it queen Iocaste for a wife."

When the Thebans heard these words, they were paralysed with fear. The bravest young men of the city had already lost their lives in trying to defeat the fearsome monster. Was anyone left who would dare approach the Sphinx, when it was common knowledge he would be walking straight into the jaws of death?

As they stood there trembling, a messenger came running in.

"Brothers!" he cried. "The Sphinx is no more! There is nothing left to be afraid of. A hero dared to face her. He solved the riddle and the monster toppled from the rock and fell to her death below."

The news was incredible. In a moment a thousand voices rose in a clamour. Some wept for joy, while others could not believe that at last the curse had been lifted from their land.

Then a huge throng came streaming through one of the great gates in the city walls, carrying Oedipus along with them, and they bore him up the steps to where Creon was standing. There was no longer any doubt: the monster was dead and this hero was the saviour of the city. Now his prize would be the throne of Thebes and the hand of queen Iocaste.

And so Oedipus, who had killed his father without knowing it, now took Laius' place and married his own mother. He was delighted at the turn events had taken, for he believed he had escaped his fate, not only for the present but for all time to come. Even so, he kept one thing in mind: he must never set foot in Corinth.

Poor, deluded Oedipus! How could you have guessed that you had already killed your father, that the marriage with your mother was now a fact – and all because you were burdened with a fate that was ordained for you before you even came into the world? Such was the will of Apollo – that Pelops' curse should take effect and Laius' hideous crime be punished.

Oedipus had four children by Iocaste: two boys, Eteocles and Polyneices and two girls, Antigone and Ismene.

Thus the final part of the oracle was fulfilled: Oedipus had children by his own mother, children who were at one and the same time his brothers and sisters, too. Yet he and everybody else in Thebes was completely ignorant of the fact. Only

Teiresias, the blind seer of the city, would turn his face away whenever he sensed that Oedipus was near him, but even he said nothing.

Oedipus ruled wisely over Thebes, loved by a people who continued to look upon him as their saviour. For many years, no shadow fell upon his reign, while he considered himself the happiest of men, convinced that the gods had looked upon his deeds with favour.

Yet up on Olympus, it had not been forgotten that Labdacus' descendants must be made to pay. If that punishment was slow in coming, it was not because the outrages Oedipus had committed in his ignorance had been forgiven, or because Pelops' curse had been overlooked. If he was left, and even helped in his long climb up the stairway to earthly happiness, it was only to make his fall more horrible and his pain the more unbearable.

Yet why?

Simply to make men understand the power of the gods.

No, they did not forget the luckless Oedipus, innocent though he might be. And fate so worked that it was he himself who started to reveal the truth. When the first horrible glimmerings of that truth appeared, he was the one who wanted it laid bare in all its horror, and stubbornly insisted that full light be shed on it, not counting the price that he would pay. And since the pangs of conscience always torture the innocent far more sharply than the guilty, he condemned himself by his own insistence to a punishment harsher perhaps than any mortal had ever had to bear.

All this is told in Sophocles' immortal tragedy 'King Oedipus', on which the tale that follows has been based.

KING OEDIPUS

after Sophocles

Dark days had fallen upon Thebes again – worse, even, than when the city had lived in terror of the dreadful Sphinx. Once more its people were plunged into despair. From the altars of the gods, the smoke of offerings rose high into the sky, and all around were heard the entreaties of the priests and the groans of the Thebans as they suffered and died beneath the weight of this unbearable new burden.

At their wits' end, the elders of the city, led by the priests of Zeus, had gathered before the palace of king Oedipus. They had been joined by a crowd of younger men and children, and fear and anguish were written on every face. They all carried sacred branches, which they laid with fervent pleas before the altars to the gods which stood outside the palace. Then they went down on their knees before the great main gate.

Oedipus came out of the palace, his face drawn with pain, and looking down upon the crowd he asked them in a troubled voice:

"My children, descendants of old Cadmus, why do you kneel in prayer before the altars and lay the sacred branches on them? I saw you gathering and knew that I must come in person to find out what you want. So tell me, reverend sir," he asked the priest of Zeus, "since you are best fitted to speak on everyone's behalf, why are you here? Tell me, and I shall do whatever you request of me, for I can see the anguish which has brought you to your knees."

"Mighty Oedipus," replied the priest, "these frail children here, and these, the flower of our youth, and these, whom the long years have bent and withered, and I, the priest of Zeus, have fallen on our knees before your altars. The rest of your people are bent in prayer in the squares below, before the two temples of Athena and the prophetic altar of Ismenus. For our city is reeling from the blows that strike our land. The crops are drooping on the plain, the herds are being carried off by sickness and our women giving birth to children that are dead before they leave the womb. Alas, that is not all, for Apollo has loosed a fearsome sickness on us which is wiping out your people. There is not a house that does not echo with our wails of grief, and Hades is loud with the sad cries and groans of the Thebans who have died. That is why we have come to you now, suppliants before your family altars, old men, young men and children all together, for we believe you are the only man who has the power to save us. You may not be the equal of the gods, but you are the first and wisest in the city. Just as you once saved us from the cruel Sphinx, so now you will find a way to save us once again, either by calling on the gods for aid or by the might of your own powers. That is why we kneel at your feet and beg you, Oedipus, to save our city from the great evil that has fallen on it, before Thebes is destroyed completely; for neither castle nor the strongest ship of war has any worth if none are left to man it."

"My sons," the king replied, "I know what Thebes is suffering. I know your anguish and your misery. But you should know my sufferings are worse than yours. The pain I feel is not just for myself but for the city as a whole. Nor do you find me unprepared, for I have shed bitter tears these many days past, racking my brains to find some way the city may be saved. I have decided the first thing we should do is find out why the gods are angry with us. For that reason, I have sent

Creon, the brother of my wife Iocaste, to the Oracle at Delphi, there to seek the help of the god Apollo. Creon set off on his mission many days ago, and I am anxious, for by now he should have returned. When he does so, bringing with him the words of the oracle, may I be doubly cursed if I do not act upon the god's advice."

Hardly had Oedipus finished speaking when Creon appeared upon the scene. A smile was on his face, and all guessed that there was indeed a way of saving Thebes.

"Tell us, brother," cried Oedipus as Creon drew near, "what message have you brought to us from Delphi? Good or bad?"

"Any message is good when it tells you what to do," Creon replied. "And if we achieve the task the god demands, all will go well with us."

"Don't keep us in suspense, then. Speak out in front of everybody here, for their fate grieves me more than any troubles of my own."

Then Creon said: "The god decrees that we must cleanse our land of a foul miasma which has infected it. We must cast out the murderer or wipe the slaying clean by killing the offender in his turn, for it is the victim's blood which hovers over the city like a poisonous mist."

"But of what victim and what murderer does the oracle speak?" asked Oedipus in bewilderment.

"Laius was king once in these lands," Creon replied.

"I know that, but I never met him."

"Since he was the victim who was slain, the god commands that we punish the murderer, if we wish to be saved from the ill-fortune that is afflicting us."

"How can we uncover the traces of such an old killing?"

"When one seeks hard enough, one finds. Truth escapes those who fail to search for it."

"Indeed it does. But tell me, where did Laius meet his death?"

"He was on his way to the oracle, to ask how we might be delivered from the Sphinx. He never returned."

"Was there nobody who saw what happened? Did he have no escort?"

"Yes, but all of them were killed save one. And he could tell us little."

"What did he say, though? The slightest clue would give us hope."

"Robbers did the killing, so he said. A band of them, not just one man."

"Would robbers dare to kill a king, if someone in the city had not put them up to it? We must search in that direction."

"That was just what we suspected. We looked into the matter, but those were such troubled days, perhaps we did not investigate as fully as we should have done. The Sphinx's reign of terror was foremost in our thoughts, and so we accepted the survivor's story at face value."

"Now, however, by the grace of the gods, it is I who rule over Thebes," declared king Oedipus, "and I will have the truth revealed. The god was right to care about the dead man. I will back you to the hilt, to see our city cleansed of the foul miasma which hangs over it. This I shall do not only out of obligation towards the victim, but for my own sake as well. For who is to say that the man who murdered Laius may not want to do away with me in turn? Send out a herald to gather all our people here. Leave everything in my hands, and with the help of Apollo I believe we may be saved. Yet even if we are destroyed, that, too, will be the will of the god."

When Oedipus had spoken, the priest cried out:

"Rise, children! For our king, the man who saved us once, has promised us his aid. And may Phoebus Apollo, who sent us this message from his oracle, become our saviour and set a term upon our sufferings."

Slowly the crowd broke up, and Creon went off with them. Fifteen of the elders remained behind and advanced until they were standing face to face with Oedipus. Then they broke into this chant:

> *Ah, what words are these which echo,*
> *From Delphi rich in gleaming gold,*
> *Offered to Thebes the seven-gated!*

My mind spins and my body trembles.
Delian Apollo, I fear lest
You ask more of us, and yet more.
Tell us, O heavenly voice, O tell us!
Set our troubled minds at rest.

First to you I bow, Athena,
Immortal daughter of great Zeus,
After to you, Phoebus Apollo,
And to your sister, Artemis,
Whose golden throne our square adorns.
Kneeling before you three, we beg you
to save us in our hour of need.
And as you brought us safe through fire,
Cast this new evil far from us.

Drive Ares, savage god of battle,
Who falls on us with clashing arms,
Drive him far away from us,
Far, far across the broad-waved sea
To the cold, distant gulf of Thrace,
Far, far away from our warm lands.
And you, almighty father Zeus,
Who thunder and bright lightning wield,
Destroy this evil with your bolts!

> *And Bacchus, guardian of our lands,*
> *With your bright golden diadem*
> *Which sparkles like the new-tapped wine,*
> *Become our ally and our friend*
> *and with your blazing torches' fire*
> *Fall vengefully upon that god*
> *Who worshippers on earth has none*
> *And does not know the name of honour!*

"Reverend elders of Thebes," said Oedipus in reply, "your entreaties to the gods shall not go unheard, provided that each of us does all that lies within his power, starting with me. Although I am not a native of these parts and cannot have been involved in a murder which was committed before I even came to Thebes, it is my duty as king to find the guilty man who has caused this poisonous cloud to spread over our land. Listen, then, to my command: Let any man who knows the murderer of Laius speak up without fear, for I shall protect him, he will receive a fitting reward, and the whole city will be forever grateful. Even if the killer is here and is afraid to come forward and confess, let him not fear to present himself before me, for he will suffer no other punishment than banishment. But if there is anyone who knows and keeps his silence, either for others' sake or for his own, then I lay my curse upon that man. Let no person in this country give him

... Ah, what words are these which echo...

hearth-room, nor any speak to him, nor any offer sacrifices with him to the gods, nor even give him so much as a drop of water. Let every citizen cast him out instead, so that in no corner of this land will he find sympathy or aid. For he is the foul miasma that the oracle of Apollo has revealed to us. Yes, such an ally will I prove to the god and to the murdered king! May the man who committed that vile deed come to an end that is even viler still. As for myself, I have but this to say: If the murderer comes to my house and I recognize him for what he is but do not denounce him, then may all the curses I have just invoked fall upon me instead. I demand of all of you that you carry out what I command, for the sake of the god, for the sake of our country which is dying, and, yes, even for the sake of your king, who saved you once. For it is my duty to fight on the murdered man's behalf as if he were my father, to seek out the slayer of the son of Labdacus, who sprang from the blood of mighty Cadmus, founder of Thebes. I implore the gods to strike down those who ignore my orders with punishments even harsher than the ones we labour under now. As for those who lend a willing ear to my commands and help to find the murderer, may the gods be at their side for ever."

When Oedipus had spoken, the most respected of the city's elders stepped forward and announced:

"Since you have bound us with such curses without our knowing who the killer is, it would seem that the only one who can help us find the guilty party is Apollo himself. But then again, no one can force a god to reveal things that he does not wish to. Nothing is left to us but to ask the seer Teiresias, the only person amongst mortals who, though blind, sees far, and knows many things that none of us is party to."

"I have not neglected to do so, reverend sir," replied king Oedipus. "Creon advised me I should send for him and I told him to dispatch two heralds with the message. I am surprised he is not here already."

"But here he comes!" cried the elders. "O Teiresias, save the city from destruction!" And they stood aside to let the blind man pass, as a child led him in.

When he drew near, Oedipus said to him:

"Come, Teiresias, the city needs you now as never before, for to you both things known and unknown are revealed. You cannot see, but you can sense as we do the calamity which has befallen us. Not long ago, I received an oracle from Delphi which says that if we wish to be saved from the curse the gods have laid upon us, we must find those who killed king Laius and either kill them in their turn or drive them far from this land. That is why we have called you here – to tell us if you know anything which you have learnt by the power of your divining art, and to beg you not to refuse to reveal it to us. Reverend seer, we now place all our hopes in you, and we look to your powers of divination for the salvation of the city.

Help us, Teiresias, to dispel this evil shadow from our land. What could be finer than to help your people with all the powers of your knowledge?"

The great seer heard Oedipus out with lowered head and a frown upon his face.

"It is a terrible thing to have knowledge of the truth when no good can come of it," he finally replied. "I should have guessed what you would ask of me, and then I never would have come here."

"You astonish me," replied Oedipus. "I had counted on your help."

"Yet I prefer to return home. It is the best course for us both."

"Teiresias, this city raised you. Such words will not be pleasing to it."

"If I say what I know, it will be the end of you. I do not wish to suffer the same fate, and so I had best be on my way."

"In the name of all the gods, stay! We beg you on our bended knees!"

"Only because you know not what you ask. You will never learn the awful truth from me. Besides, there is no need for me to tell it."

"What are you saying, Teiresias? You know, but will not tell? You mean you could save this city and yet refuse to do so?"

..."It is a terrible thing to have knowledge of the truth when
no good can come of it"...

"I would be sorry for you if I did tell, and for myself as well. So no more questions – for you will get nothing from me."

"Now we all see you for the miserable creature that you are! Hard-hearted and stubborn!"

"You only say that because you do not see your own stubbornness."

"The very stones would rise, Teiresias, to hear you talking in this way, with such cruel lack of feeling for your city."

"Do not be angry. You will learn what must be learned whether I speak or not."

"Then why should you not tell me, since I will learn in any case?"

"I cannot. Rage at me all you will, but do not imagine you will force me in this way to reveal what I do not wish to."

"This time you have driven me too far! Do you think I have not noticed how you have always avoided me? Now I understand the reason why you do not wish to speak. You were behind this crime! If you were not blind, I'd say you murdered Laius with your own hands, for now it's clear you are capable of worse things still."

"Ah, so! How dare you address me in this fashion, when you yourself are the foul miasma which has tainted this land of ours?"

"Have you no shame? Or do you think you can escape this

way?"

"There is no longer any reason to escape. I have told the truth."

"And where did you find this truth of yours? Not in your seeing powers, for sure!"

"You drove me to it. If I spoke out, it was only because you provoked me."

"And what, exactly, did you say? Repeat it, so I can hear better."

"You did not understand my words, you mean? Or do you just want me to repeat them louder?"

"You insulted me most vilely. That much I understood."

"It was no insult. I only spoke the truth. And now I shall give it you again, as you deserve. The murderer you seek is none other but yourself."

"A second insult, villain? Do you think you will get away with this unpunished?"

"I have more to tell you, and it will make you angrier still."

"Tell as many foolish stories as you like. You are wasting your breath."

"Then I say you are linked in filthy union with your nearest relative and do not even realize what a dunghill you are wallowing in."

"Enjoy yourself! Spew out your filth while you still have time!"

"If the truth has any power, you will not be able to hurt me."

"Oh, yes, the truth has power, but not on the lips of a blind man who is blind to reason, too!"

"Which of us two is the blinder, the whole world will soon find out."

"You live in the blackest darkness, and I would pity you if I did not see your evil cunning. Yet tell me, did you fabricate these lies alone, or with the help of Creon?"

"Creon, you say? Why, he has never harmed you! You sank into the mire all by yourself."

"Ah, kingly power, what envy you can breed! Yes, that is it! What ruler, and what saviour of his people does not have jealous enemies? See what has been hatched now – a glaring plot! My wife's brother, Creon, hiding behind pretended friendship, has all the time been digging my grave, using as his tool this sly magician, who only thinks of money and is a mere charlatan when it comes to visionary powers. Tell us, false seer, when did you ever once foretell the truth? How come that when the Sphinx was preying on us with her riddle you could not find the right answer, for all the divination that you claimed? No, it was left to me, an ignoramus with no powers but the quickness of his mind, to close her mouth and save the people of this land. And now, following Creon's orders, you are doing your utmost to have that saviour driven out, in the hope of widening your influence when your master takes the throne. You'll repent your treachery, the pair of you. He for plotting this, and you, foolish old man, for following him."

"We believe that both men speak in anger," said the city elders. "We should pay them no attention. How to find what the god demands of us is all that should concern us now."

"Yes, but insults must be answered," Teiresias insisted. "I have that right, for I am no slave of Oedipus but the humble servant of Apollo. And so I tell you, king, since you choose to mock my blindness, that it is you whose eyes have lost their light, since you cannot see how low you have fallen, whose throne you are seated on or whom you share the palace with. Do you know who your parents are, I wonder? And have you ever thought that you are the deadly enemy of those closest to you, both those who have gone down to Hades and those who are still upon the earth? Can you imagine, too, what curse will fall upon you, casting you into the blackest darkness? And can you foresee that your cries of grief and loathing will echo through the city when you learn who it was that you once murdered, what woman you married, and that your children by her stand in another blood-bond to you also? No? Then while you still hold power, heap insults on myself and Creon, for soon you will fall deeper than any man has ever fallen before."

"Go back to your master, fellow! Why do I sit here and listen to you?"

"You called me here, Oedipus."

"Because I could not guess that you would speak such evil nonsense."

"To you I may seem foolish, but to those who bore you I shall prove a seer indeed."

"What are you trying to say? Who brought me into the world?"

"When you learn that, all will be lost."

"Speak clearly, Teiresias!"

"You pass for a wise man. Can you not understand my meaning yet?"

"So now you make fun of me as well. Have I then no value in your eyes? Or is it a lie that thanks to my intelligence I gained this throne?"

"Only to be toppled from it, lower than any king has ever fallen."

"So be it. It is enough to me to know I saved the city."

"Yet you will curse the day that you were born. But it is time that I was on my way. Boy, lead me out of here."

"Go, then, and good riddance to you! Let me never see your face again!"

"Don't worry. I shall go. But since you provoke me I shall reveal everything. I tell you that the murderer of Laius stands here before me and that he is no foreigner but a Theban who will not rejoice when he discovers it. This same man now has his sight and is powerful and rich, but he will end up blinded, poor and weak, groping his dark way in alien lands. He will by then have learned that to his children he is father and brother all at once, to his wife both husband and son at the same time, and to his father both sharer of his marriage bed and his murderer, too. Think these things over when you go back into the palace, and if you find I am a liar, then you may call me a charlatan and not a seer."

With these words, he stretched a faltering hand out to the boy who was to guide him. As he left, Oedipus walked back into the palace, his head still buzzing with the great seer's words, but his mind as yet unable to grasp how prophetic those words were. Meanwhile, the troubled elders of the city were unable to keep silence longer.

> *How can we begin to believe*
> *That Oedipus is an evil man?*
> *How can our ruler be the cloud*
> *Of evil, poisoning our land?*
> *He who by strength of mind alone*
> *Struck down the Sphinx, the scourge of Thebes?*
> *How can we call him traitor now,*
> *How abandon our one last hope*

Of saving our city from this curse?

We owe respect to Teiresias,
Yet only Zeus and Apollo know
The fate of mortals here on earth.
Seers are simply men like us;
Any of them can make mistakes,
And that wisdom can prove superior
To any seer's divining powers
Is a lesson the years have taught us all.
We do not suspect you, Oedipus.
We harbour no evil thoughts of you.

No sooner had the chorus finished than Creon stormed in, protesting:

"Citizens of Thebes! I hear the king has levelled slanderous accusations at me. I have come here to learn if it is true."

"Yes, it is true," replied the first among the elders. "But what he said was uttered in rage. He was not thinking when he spoke."

"Yet if he charged that I plotted with the seer to feed him with false prophecies, that is a terrible accusation he lays on me, and all the world will take me for a conspirator. How could he have uttered such wild words?"

"It is not for me to judge his meaning. But look, here he is, coming out of the palace."

"You, fellow!" shouted Oedipus, "How dare you show your face before my doors, acting the friend as bold as brass, yet plotting my downfall all the while? Perhaps you thought I would never learn about your wicked plan and you would get away with it. Are you so foolish as to think that you could snatch my powers from me, powers that the people do not bestow on the first-comer but only on him who has the wealth, intelligence and strength to wield them?"

"Oedipus, you accuse me without letting me speak!"

"I know that if I did you would only worm your way out craftily."

"Yet you must hear me."

"What, hear you say you are no villain?"

"Obstinacy is a bad counsellor."

"I have proofs."

"Let me hear them."

"Did you not press me, Creon, to summon this seer of yours?"

"And I was right to do so."

"Tell me now, how many years have passed since Laius was slain?"

"It has been many years."

"And was Teiresias a seer in those days?"

"Just as he is now, and just as well-respected."

"Well now, did he ever say anything concerning me?"

"Not that I know of, no."

"And you never tried to lay your hands on Laius' murderer?"

"It was as I have already told you. We tried, but there was nothing to be learned."

"How come this wise Teiresias of yours did not point the finger at the killer all those years ago?"

"That I do not know."

"And why does he identify him now?"

"I do not know what he has just been saying."

"He has been saying precisely what you two agreed upon! That I killed Laius."

"If that is what he says, I only have your word for it. But now I think I have the right to ask you something in my turn."

"Ask what you will. You'll never make a murderer of me!"

"Am I or am I not the brother of the queen?"

"You are. There is no denying that."

"And does she share equal power with you over this land?"

"Her wish is my command."

"And am I not next in line, in power and honour?"

"Till now you were. But you have proved unfaithful."

"I have not, and to have broken faith would be insane. Think about it. Which is to be preferred: to rule in fear or to enjoy untroubled sleep yet still have all the power and privileges of

... "Obstinacy is a bad counsellor"...

a ruler? By nature I am one of those who would always choose
the second. Do I not have everything? What more could I
desire? I am shown marks of respect wherever I go, and all
who seek some special favour of you come to me first, for it
is in my hands whether you will grant their wishes. Why
should I give up such a life to strive for higher things and
become evil by the gaining of them? If you want proof, just
go to the oracle yourself and ask if the message that it gave
was the one that I passed on to you. If you learn that I changed
it, or still more, that I plotted against you, then kill me – and
you can add my own vote of condemnation to the voices raised
against me. For it is not right or just to call the evil good and
the honest man a villain before you have examined all the
evidence – and woe betide the man who thrusts his faithful
friends aside."

"He has spoken wisely, king," the elders said. "Do not decide over-quickly. Terrible mistakes can be made when one
acts in haste."

"Yes, but when one is in haste and the other dawdles, it is
not hard to see who will win and who will lose."

"Say what you want, then" Creon cried. "Is it exile you
have in mind?"

"Something worse. The only punishment suitable for traitors."

"You cannot have me killed until you prove these accusations."

"Who are you to tell me what to do? You, who raised your hand against the ruler you were bound in duty to obey?"

"How can I not, when I see that your judgement has been clouded?"

"No, my judgement is crystal-clear, and it tells me you are rotten to the core!"

"And if you are labouring under some terrible delusion?"

"Why, even then you have no choice but to obey me."

"I will not be the victim of an injustice!"

"Do you hear what he says, the villain?"

"I hold power in this city too! You are not the only ruler!"

"Calm down, your majesties, calm down!" the chief elder implored. "Here comes queen Iocaste, and fortunately just in time. With her help, try to resolve your differences."

"Why, oh why?" Iocaste cried, "Why let your tempers flare when there is trouble enough to afflict us in this kingdom as it is? Get inside, Oedipus – and you, Creon, leave, before your passions get the better of you!"

"Sister," cried Creon, "your husband here is calling for my death!"

"Because I caught him plotting to cast me from the throne."

"By Zeus! May I be cursed if I even thought of doing such a thing!"

"Respect that oath, Oedipus, for it is not lightly sworn,"

Iocaste warned. "Besides, you must consider my opinion, and the elders'."

"Yes, king," their leader added, "all of us here beg you not to act in haste."

"What would you have me do, then?"

"You must not lay hands on a man who has given his solemn word."

"In other words, you are asking me to sign my own death-warrant!"

"By the god Helius, no! May I meet the worst of deaths if ever such a thought should cross my mind. Yet to see this land of ours weighed down with new miseries is more than my old heart can bear."

"Very well, then. I shall respect your wishes, since you express them with such anguish in your voice. I shall not harm this fellow, even if it costs me my life or shameful banishment. But I shall go on hating him, even from the underworld."

"You submit unwillingly, I see," said Creon. "Yet when your anger passes you will bitterly regret your words, for you are not an evil man. Men like you bring punishment upon themselves."

"Be silent! Leave me now, for I cannot even bear to look at you."

"I am going. You have treated me unjustly, but I know these others feel for me." With these words, Creon turned on his heel and strode off, boiling with indignation.

Then Iocaste said, "Tell me, my lord, in the name of all the gods, why such bitter rage?"

"Since I respect you above all others, I shall tell you why. Then you will see how faithless Creon has proved."

"Tell me. I want to know why you accuse him."

"For slandering me and plotting my overthrow! He says it was I who murdered Laius!"

"My own brother said such a thing?"

"He sent that charlatan of a seer to announce it."

"What seer? There's not a man on earth who really has such powers, and if you don't believe me, listen to this: King Laius once received an oracle – I can't say it came directly from Apollo, but at least from one of his priests – telling him he was fated to meet death at his son's hands. Yet by all accounts he was killed by robbers at a crossroads, while as for the son, before he was even three days old, he bound him by the ankles and gave orders for the little mite to be abandoned on some wild mountainside. So you see, the god neither allowed the son to grow up to be his father's murderer, nor the father to meet his death in the way that he had feared. That's why I tell you to pay no heed to seers and prophecies, for what the gods do not wish to stay hidden will come to light some day in any case."

"Ah, wife! These words make me sick at heart to hear! My

head is spinning!"

"But what have I said to make you act like this?"

"Did you not say that Laius was murdered at a crossroads?"

"That's what they said then, and the story hasn't changed."

"And where is this place?"

"Where the road to Delphi crosses a track which leads to Daulis."

"And how long is it since this evil deed took place?"

"Shortly before you became king of Thebes."

"Zeus! What fate do you have in store for me?"

"Why do you look so anguished, husband?"

"Do not ask, I beg you. Just tell me about Laius. How old was he? What did he look like?"

"He was tall, his hair was just beginning to go grey, and in appearance he was not unlike yourself."

"Oh, ye gods! I fear that all the curses I have uttered are about to fall on me!"

"Husband, what are you saying? Your wild look terrifies me!"

"I am afraid the blind man is a seer, after all. Yet tell me..."

"I shall tell you anything you ask, but you are frightening me."

"How many men were with the king?"

"Four, with the fellow who escaped, and one charioteer."

"Oh, death! Now it is all clear. And the news, of course,

was brought by the one who got away?"

"Yes, he was a slave of ours."

"And is he in the palace now, by any chance?"

"No, when he saw that you were to be king, he entreated me on bended knee to send him out onto the plain to join the herdsmen, far from the city limits, and I granted his request, since he had always been a faithful servant."

"Could he be brought here straight away?"

"I'll have him sent for. But what could you want with this man?"

"What do I want with him? Haven't I revealed enough already?"

"Then he shall come. Meanwhile, I think you owe it to me to say what weighs upon your soul."

"Owe it to you? Why there is no one in the world who more deserves to hear how I have fallen into such misfortune! I shall hide nothing from you, wife. My father was Polybus of Corinth, and my mother Merope. All of my fellow-citizens held me in esteem, until an incident occurred which changed my life. At a feast, some drunken guest taunted me with not being my father's real son. When I had given him the answer he deserved, I took my parents aside and questioned them, to make sure it wasn't true. They were furious at the shameless way the fellow had insulted me, and seeing their anger I breathed a sigh of relief. Yet I was eaten by curiosity, and that little worm of doubt would give me not a moment's rest. So I decided to seek an answer from the oracle at Delphi, without letting my parents know. Apollo did not answer the question that I put to him, but revealed to me instead that I was burdened with a heavy curse, being doomed to be my father's murderer, to marry my own mother and to have children that men could never bear to look upon. When I heard this, I looked by the stars to see where Corinth lay, then set off in the opposite direction, so that these awful prophecies could never come to pass. In my flight, I reached the place where you told me Laius had been killed. And as for what happened next, I shall tell you all. At that cursed crossroads, then, I met a herald, and behind him a splendid four-wheeled chariot, drawn by young horses. In that chariot sat a man just like the one you have described to me. As I drew near, the charioteer and the older man haughtily ordered me to get out of the way, and cursed me, too. Insulted by their manner, I did not leave the road but kept on walking so that the chariot could pass me to one side. The way was narrow, and as they came abreast, the older man, who had been waiting for me, lifted his arm and laid his heavy whip across my face. The punishment he received in return was far, far worse. In self-defence, I lunged at him full-force with my staff. He was flung back from the chariot and landed dead upon the rocks. The others then threw themselves on me, and I dispatched them,

... "if that stranger whom I killed was Laius, I am
the unhappiest of men"...

too. Now if that stranger whom I killed was Laius, I am the unhappiest of men. Who could be more hateful to the gods, especially after the heavy curses which my own lips uttered against his murderer? 'Let no man greet him or receive him,' I said, 'but let all cast him out, for he is the foul miasma which is poisoning this land'. I am that man. Not only did I slay Laius, but I corrupt his wife with the very hands that took his life. Foul killer that I am, I have no choice but to flee my second homeland as I fled the first, for I cannot return to Corinth lest the oracle prove true and I strike down my own father and marry the woman who brought me into the world. All I now beg the gods is not to make me go on living if other hideous evils are fated to defile me. Truly, what demon is it, what cruel-hearted god, that pursues me so relentlessly?"

Overwhelmed by all that she had heard, Iocaste was at a loss for words. The chorus of the elders stood in open-mouthed surprise as well, until the oldest of them broke the shocked silence, saying:

"Your majesty, do not abandon all hope before the witness to the murder has arrived."

"Yes, I still have hope, until the herdsman comes to shatter it."

"What hope, unlucky man?" Iocaste asked.

"If he describes what happened as you told it to me, then I am not the miasma hanging over Thebes."

"What did I say that can be of such importance?"

"You told me Laius was killed by robbers. If the man says it was a band of thieves that killed him, then I am innocent, for there is a difference between one man and many."

"But that is exactly what he said, and he cannot change his story now, for he told it before a crowd of witnesses, and not just to me. Even supposing that he gives a different version this time, there is still no proof that Laius met his death at your hands, since Apollo's oracle stated clearly that he would be killed by his own son, and that poor little creature died long before his father, on some mountainside. Do you see now why I pay so little heed to prophecies?"

"You could be right, but send now for the herdsman."

"Yes, I shall call for him immediately. Let us go in and tell a slave to bring him."

With this they went back into the palace, while the city elders, troubled by all that they had heard, began to chant:

> *Happy the ruler whom the Fates*
> *Decree shall live a virtuous life.*
> *He is protected by the laws*
> *That issue from the Olympian heights;*
> *Laws that can never be erased,*
> *Too absolute to be writ down.*

Tyrants are bred of lawlessness;
If their impiety should thrive
And raise them to the highest peaks,
It is but to cast them to such depths
Where human foot has never trod
Nor any hope of rescue lies.
The man who treads this evil path,
Exulting in unholy deeds,
Showing no fear of divine wrath,
May retribution fall on him;
And worse still on the man who dares
Lay impious hands on holy things
That none till now have dared to touch.

How can we stand with reverence
Before the oracle of the god,
And how can we beseech his help
If one by one his words prove false?

If, father Zeus, you are indeed
Mighty in power and rule all things,
Reveal that power to us now.
For the prophecies are no longer clear,
Apollo's word not held in awe,
And faith in the gods, alas, fades fast.

The chorus of the elders ended as Iocaste came out from the palace. She was holding sacred branches to lay upon the altars, and the young handmaids who accompanied her were also carrying offerings for the gods.

"Elders of the city," she announced, "I have decided to offer up these sacrifices because the king is in torments of confusion. He puts his trust in every prophecy he hears instead of looking back and drawing sensible conclusions. Since I cannot prevail on him with logic, I now seek Apollo's aid. May he give an answer that will free us all from this terrible burden of doubt."

As Iocaste was laying her offerings upon the altar, a stranger arrived, went up to the elders of the city and said:

"Reverend elders, does king Oedipus live in this palace? It is vital that I see him."

"This is his palace, stranger. The king himself is within," was the reply, "and here is queen Iocaste, his wife and the mother of his children."

"May you live in peace, your majesty, surrounded by your happy subjects, and a worthy partner to your noble lord."

"May I wish you likewise, stranger, for by your kind words you deserve to. Where are you from, and what brings you to our city?"

"I come from Corinth, and with news that I believe will

bring you joy, not sorrow. Oedipus is the new king of Corinth, since old Polybus is no longer with us."

"Do you mean he's dead?" asked Iocaste in surprise.

"Upon my life, he is indeed."

"Run, child, and tell this to your master," cried Iocaste to a handmaiden. "Ah, what price prophecy now! The man that Oedipus was so terrified of killing has died a natural death, and not by his son's hand."

Oedipus came at once.

"Tell me, beloved wife," he asked, "why did you send for me – and who's this stranger here?"

"This man has come from Corinth to tell us that your father, Polybus, is dead."

"What's that, stranger? Say it again. I want to hear it from your own lips."

"Then I repeat my words, and mark them well: Polybus is no more."

"What did he die of?" Oedipus enquired. "Was it from sickness or did he fall by a murderer's hand?"

"It does not take much to bring an old man to his bed."

"You mean it was illness that carried him off?"

"Yes, and what could be more natural at his age?"

"Poor father!" Oedipus exclaimed. "Now you lie beneath the ground without my lifting a murderer's sword against you, unless it was your grief at losing me which hastened your

... "Polybus is no more"...

end. In any case, you have gone from us in ripe old age and taken with you the prophecies which tortured us so long when all the while they were not worth believing."

"Did I not tell you so, Oedipus?" rejoined Iocaste.

"You did, but I let myself be ruled by my fears."

"Now you must cast all those terrors from your mind."

"And not even tremble at the marriage that they speak of?"

"Do you mean to say you still are not convinced that everything which happens, happens by chance? No one can foretell the future without falling into error, and yet you sit there fearing you may one day be married to your mother. How many men have not dreamt of such a thing? Yet have those dreams even once turned out to be prophetic? You mark my word: If you want to lead a happy life, pay no attention to prophecies."

"Everything you say is perfectly reasonable, yet as long as my mother lives I shall have cause to fear."

"Hasn't your father's death persuaded you otherwise?"

"Not yet. Until my mother dies, it is my duty to be cautious."

"One moment," the stranger interrupted. "What woman is this you speak of with such terror?"

"If you do not know already, stranger, I tell you my mother is Merope."

"There are many things I know. One is a mystery to me,

though. Exactly what is it you fear?"

"There is a terrible oracle, a warning from the gods."

"Forgive me, but may I be told what it says?"

"Certainly you may. Apollo told me once that I was destined to take my father's life and marry my own mother. That is the reason why I fled from Corinth, though with a heavy heart, for I would have much preferred to go on living with my parents."

"So that is the reason why you came to this distant land?"

"Yes, so I could never be my father's murderer."

"Well, let that trouble you no more, for I can calm your fears."

"If you can do so, I will reward you handsomely."

"And I shall not refuse. To tell the truth, if I came here, it was in hope of getting something in return when you came back to Corinth."

"I shall never return to the place where I was born as long as even one of my parents is still living."

"That is because you live in ignorance of the truth."

"It is because I dread to see Phoebus Apollo's prophecy come true."

"The prophecy which says that you will sin against your mother and father?"

"Yes, that is my constant fear."

"And if I, a poor shepherd, tell you that you have no parents in Corinth, will you believe me?"

"Do you mean to say that Polybus is not my father?" asked
Oedipus in bewilderment. Iocaste was as thunderstruck as he.

"Polybus has no more claim to be your father than I do."

"But he always called me his son."

"Yet now the time has come for you to learn that it was I
who gave you to him."

"You? Then what of all the tender love he and Merope
showed me?"

"That was because they could never have children of their
own."

"What you are telling me seems incredible. Say, though,
where did you first see me?"

"In a wooded gorge on Mount Cythaeron."

"Can this be true?" the puzzled chorus of the elders mur-
mured.

"If it is true, then I am undone!" Iocaste stammered in a
broken voice. Yet her words went unheard and Oedipus per-
sisted in his fatal questioning.

"What state was I in when you found me?"

"When you were handed to me, your feet were pierced and
bound together at the ankles."

Iocaste, too, was pierced by the stranger's words, yet no
one noticed.

"So I was marked by shame from infancy," Oedipus muttered.

"And that is how you got your name, too," added the stranger: 'Oedipus the swollen-footed'.

"Who did this evil thing to me? My father or my mother?"

"That I cannot say. Perhaps the man who gave you to me can tell you."

"Who was he, do you know?"

"Some shepherd or other, a servant of king Laius."

"Can anyone here tell us who was Laius' shepherd on Mount Cythaeron in those days?"

"It is the same man that you summoned to your presence," one of the elders replied. "But the queen knows more of that than any of us."

"Ah, Oedipus, Oedipus!" Iocaste cried, her soul in torment, "Pay no heed to these words! Forget them, for your own good!"

"That cannot be. Since I bear the scars of which he speaks, I must go on and find my origins, whatever they may be."

"No, in the god's name, Oedipus! Seek no further if you love your life. Let my pain be enough for both of us."

"Do not grieve, wife, for you are in no way to blame, even if I should learn this day that I was born a slave."

"I implore you, listen to me and stop what you are doing!"

"I shall not cease until I have found out who I am."

"Unlucky man! For your own good, listen to the voice of reason!"

"And yet the voice of reason only brings me pain."

"Poor Oedipus! May you never learn your true identity!"

"Enough, Iocaste! Let someone bring the shepherd with all speed, even if your noble blood will be offended by my lowly origin."

"Alas, there is no saving you, unhappy man! These are the last words you shall hear from me!" Iocaste cried, and fled wildly back into the palace.

"Why did the queen leave in such agitation?" enquired the chief elder. "I fear that some great evil will befall us."

"Then let it! I must know the secret of my birth, however humble it may prove. Yet she, proud woman, is afraid she will be shamed, and that I understand. Yet I consider it no shame to be the child of fortune. She was my mother, and if at first she made me small and unimportant, later she raised me up to power and majesty. I became what I am, and nothing can change that. I must learn where I came from."

Then the chorus of the elders, taking courage from Oedipus' words, threw off their fears and cried:

> *If we had perfect powers of vision*
> *And understanding were given our minds,*
> *We would swear by the gods of Olympus*
> *That at tomorrow night's full moon*
> *We shall sing of the joy of Oedipus,*

Who was suckled and raised on Cythaeron.
And then by Phoebus Apollo's will
We shall take up the dance at the happy news
Of the great and unhoped-for deliverance.

What nereid gave you birth, my lord,
And who was the god who fathered you?
Was it Pan, who wanders the mountainsides,
Or Apollo, who loves the broad green fields,
Or Hermes, born in Cyllene's glades?
Or was it Bacchus, who loves to embrace
The nymphs of Helicon in the shade
Where the mountain torrents run cool and deep?

But Oedipus, whose mind had been on other things, cried out:

"Elders, see who is coming! I think it is the herdsman. I have never laid eyes on the man before, but judging from his age it must be he."

"Yes, that's the man," replied one of the elders. "He was the most trustworthy shepherd Laius had."

"You, my Corinthian friend, what do you say? Is he the one?" asked Oedipus.

"Yes, he is the one you see."

Trembling, with head bowed low, the herdsman approached. His manner alone was enough to tell Oedipus that this was the man who had escaped the slaughter at the cursed crossroads.

"Hey, you, old man!" he shouted. "Look me in the eyes and answer my questions. Were you ever a servant of king Laius?"

"Yes, your majesty, but he did not buy me. I was born and brought up here."

"And what was your job?"

"Most of the time, I grazed my master's flocks."

"What pastures did you take them to?"

"To Mount Cythaeron and the country round about."

"This man you see here – have you ever met with him before?"

"What business would he have with me?" the shepherd asked in fear, his mind on the killings at the crossroads. Then he looked at the Corinthian and began to understand. "Which man do you mean?" he stammered.

"It's not myself I'm asking you about," said Oedipus, seeing the reason for the shepherd's puzzled look. "I mean this fellow here, and I ask you if you remember ever having met with him."

"I can't recall. I don't know whether I have or not."

"Your majesty," the messenger from Corinth broke in, "it is not surprising that he has forgotten. Let me refresh his

... "did you not give a child to me, to bring up as my own?"

memory for him, though. After all, we met on Cythaeron three
summers in a row, he with his two flocks and I with one, and
when the winter-time drew in, I would lead my own beasts
down to the lowland pastures of king Polybus, while he would
round his up and drive them into Laius' folds. Don't you remember now, my friend?"

"Why, yes, I do. But it was all so long ago."

"And tell me, did you not give a child to me, to bring up as
my own?"

"What's going on here? Why do you drag this old tale up?"

"I mention it, my friend, because the baby we once saved
is this man here – the king!"

"Be gone, and hold your tongue!"

"Do not rail at the Corinthian, old man," Oedipus warned,
"for it is you who should be punished, and not him."

"Punished for what, your majesty?"

"Because you have not answered us concerning the baby
which he spoke of."

"He doesn't know what he's talking about. He's wasting
his breath!"

"You know, however, and if you do not speak of your own
free will, there are other ways of making you open your
mouth!"

"In the name of all the gods! Would you torture an old
man?"

"Bind his hands behind his back, somebody!"

"Alas! What do you wish to learn of me?"

"Is it true that you gave this man a baby boy?"

"Merciful heavens! Why did I not die that very day?"

"You will die now, old man, if you go on hiding the truth from me."

"Yet if I speak, the fate I suffer will be worse than death."

"Enough of your evasions! Will you confess or not?"

"Well, yes. I gave the child to him."

"After you had taken it from whom? Or was it your own, perhaps?"

"No, the baby was not mine. I did take it from somebody."

"From whom? Speak!"

"No, by the gods, your majesty! I have said enough already."

"It'll be the end of you if you oblige me to repeat my question."

"It was some child born in the palace of king Laius."

"A slave, or one born of his line?"

"May the gods have pity on me now. For the moment of awful truth has come, and I must speak."

"It has come for me, too, and I must hear you out."

"Hear, then: the father of the child was Laius. But your wife, the queen could tell you the whole story far better than myself."

"Was it she who gave the baby to you?"

"She was present when Laius placed it in my arms."

"Ah, miserable parents! Why did they give the infant to you, though?"

"To kill it."

"What, their own child? This is beyond belief!"

"They lived in terror of a fearsome oracle."

"And what did this oracle foretell?"

"That the same child would one day kill its father."

"Oh, ye gods! But tell me, why did you give the baby to this man?"

"Because I pitied it, my lord. If he took it away to his own country, I hoped it would be saved. Well, saved it was, but only to bring greater evil on us. For if you are indeed the one he says, then know that of all men born you are the most unfortunate."

"Alas! Now everything has come to light!, 'Light' I say? May I never see the light of day again now that it has been proved that I was born of forbidden parents, slept with a forbidden partner and killed the one I was forbidden to!"

With hanging head and shoulders slumped in despair, Oedipus shuffled back into the palace, a broken man. Dazed by the awful truth that their own evidence had brought into the light, the two shepherds sorrowfully withdrew and went their separate ways. Outside the palace, only the chorus of the elders now remained. The time had come for them to break into sad song.

> *O, generations of mortal men,*
> *See what a thread our life hangs by!*
> *Till now, we have never known a man*
> *Who was blessed with good fortune till the end.*
> *All we see is the ease with which*
> *One can fall from the very heights of bliss*
> *To the bottom-most rung of the ladder of life.*
> *Look at the luckless Oedipus now*
> *And say if we do not speak the truth.*
>
> *For he was the hero of heroes once,*
> *He was the man who crushed the beast*
> *With slashing talons and riddles that slew.*
> *He was the man who stood firm as a rock*
> *To save his people, and earned their praise*
> *And the throne of Thebes with its seven gates.*
> *See how ill fate has brought him down!*
> *In all our long years on this earth,*
> *We have never seen one to be pitied more.*
>
> *O, star-crossed ruler! Victim of fate!*
> *Your fortune decreed you should slay your sire*

And lie with your mother in his bed.
What long, cruel years that bed remained dumb
When the children it gave you were brother and son,
Daughter and sister; till time's wheel came full turn,
The black truth shone forth, and all was learned.
O, son of Laius, better for us
We had never known you, for now our hearts
Bleed for the man who gave us light
Yet burdened us with unbearable pain.

The chorus had hardly finished their mournful chanting, when a man suddenly came rushing out of the palace.

"Elders of Thebes!" he cried. "Brace yourselves for the frightful news. Not even the waters of the river Istrus would suffice to wash the palace clean of all the evils that have come to light so far, and what I have to tell to you now."

"Alas! What new horrors must we hear?"

"First, that the divine Iocaste is no more."

"Unhappy woman! How did she die?"

"By her own hand. Horror piled on horror! I saw it all with my own eyes. The queen came rushing into the palace, tearing her hair out with both hands, and made straight for her bed-chamber. She slammed the door behind her, all the while crying out for Laius, who has been dead for years. Through her strangled sobs, we could hear the luckless woman curs-

... "his great happiness turned to pain and darkness,
death and humiliation!"...

ing the bed on which she had borne a husband by her husband and children by her child, children all tainted by an unnatural union. After that, nothing more was heard. As I stood there, fearing the worst, Oedipus came staggering in with heart-rending cries, and we all stared at him in terror. Suddenly, he began to run here and there as if he had gone mad. Wheeling round on us, he demanded in a wild voice to know where Iocaste was. Seeing the foam that bubbled from his mouth, and his demented look, we were afraid to tell him. But some god must have whispered in his ear, for with a savage cry he hurled himself at the chamber doors, which burst wide open. Oh, what a hideous sight then met our eyes! Iocaste was hanging lifeless from the roof-beam and the king stumbled towards her with strangled moans of grief. He loosed the knot and the miserable woman tumbled to the floor. But worse was still to come! The king pulled out the golden pin which had adorned her robe and stabbed it savagely into his eyes, again and yet again, crying out all the while: 'There, eyes, take that, and that, so you cannot see the evil which has spread around me, the evil which I did myself; and so you cannot look on those who are forbidden to you!' Howling such curses, the luckless king blinded himself, doubling and tripling the misfortunes which had struck the house of Labdacus. So his great happiness turned to pain and darkness, death and humiliation! Alas, could any disaster worse than this befall a man?"

"And what is the poor fellow doing now?"

"He has ordered them to open the palace gates and lead him out. He insists that all of Thebes should see the father-killer, the monster who married his own mother, the miasma who has tainted the whole city by the hideous curses his fate has smeared him with. He demands now to be banished and cast out from the city. Yet the poor man needs help, for he is in a pitiful state. You will see him in a moment. Look, the gates are opening, and he is a sight to soften the heart of his worst enemy!"

As the gates swung open and Oedipus appeared, the chorus of the elders recoiled in horror. Unable to restrain themselves before the dreadful spectacle, they exclaimed:

> *What frenzy struck at you, unlucky man,*
> *Adding new miseries to those ills*
> *The fates already held in store for you?*
> *Alas, we do not have the heart to ask.*
> *Our eyes cannot abide to look on you,*
> *So hideous is the sight.*

"Woe on me, miserable creature that I am!" wailed Oedipus. "O, fate, how you have ruined me! O, black cloud, how grim you spread before me! O, wounds, inflicted on me by my very hands, and my own evil deeds!"

"Ah, miserable man, your pain and suffering are doubly cruel, indeed," said the leader of the elders.

"Is there any creature in the world can pity me, after the vile acts I have committed, wretch that I am?"

"How can I not feel pity, when I see you brought so low? But tell me, how did you steel yourself to take the light from your own eyes? What god drove you to such violence?"

"It was Apollo who plunged me into misery beyond belief. But as for my eyes, I struck at them unaided. No other power guided my hand. There is nothing left in this world that I can bear to look on, nothing I could see and love. Just drive me from your gates with all speed possible, so I do not befoul this land a moment longer – I, Oedipus the thrice cursed, he whom the gods chose to hate above all others on this earth."

"Yet my heart bleeds for you, Oedipus, for I cannot forget what good things you have done for all of us."

"A curse on him who saved me from an early death. Had I perished on the mountain, I would not have been able to harm anyone."

"What you say would indeed have been the best of all."

"Had I died then, I would not have become my father's murderer or come to be the husband of the woman who bore me. Yet such was my fate, that even if there had been misfortunes worse than those which struck, I would have suffered them as well."

Why live in darkness, though? Would not death be better?"

"I did what I had to. For if I had not gouged out my eyes, how could I have looked my father in the face when I went down to Hades? How could I have met my mother's gaze, when I did both of them such harm no punishment could match it? I could not even bear to see Thebes and its people, nor look upon its sacred monuments, for all the happiness I have known in this city. How could I, who pronounced such curses on the murderer of Laius, have faced you all with an untroubled gaze? Ah, Cythaeron, why did you help me? Why did you not just leave me on your slopes to die? And you, Polybus and Merope, and the old courts of Corinth I believed were mine by right of birth, why did you shelter me and raise me up? Oh, why? Only to show the world how foul I am, and of what evil seed? O, crossroads and that lonely gorge which drank my father's blood, spilled by my hands; do you, I wonder, still recall the dreadful deeds I did that day? O, you two marriages, you first that gave me birth, and you second that put my seed in the same womb, bringing forth father, brothers, children all from the same bride – her husband's very mother! Such words should not be spoken! Hide me somewhere or throw me in the sea, so the foul miasma men call Oedipus can disappear for ever!"

"I am not the one to ask. Here comes Creon, though; he is

now the highest in the land."

"Alas, what can I say, when I treated him so unjustly?"

"No, Oedipus," Creon replied, "I will not blame you for the way you spoke to me, but someone must lead you back into the palace. You are too foul a sight for the sun, the rain or mother Earth to look upon."

"That is my own wish, too, and I have another. Banish me from the land this instant. Send me to some remote spot where no human voice will greet me."

"I do not wish to act in haste. I would prefer to receive Apollo's oracle first, for these are difficult times through which we pass. Yet I have no desire to treat you harshly if it is not called for."

"However hard you are on me, I have deserved it. But as for her who lies within, make sure she has a proper burial. Cast me upon the mountainside, high up on Cythaeron, to perish where I should have perished all those years ago, had the gods not wished to save me for a viler end. Now, Creon, I have another favour to ask of you. It is for my children. The boys will need no special protection, for they are young men now and can take care of themselves. But the girls, poor creatures, have never even done the simplest task without my help, and so I beg you, be a father to them, for you are now their only guardian. Allow them to approach so I may hug them one last time. If you do me that kindness, it will seem as if we are embracing just as in the days when I had sight. But hold a moment – do I not hear them somewhere close, and crying?"

"Yes they are here. I let them come because they implored me to, and I knew that you would want it."

"Creon, I wish you every happiness for this kindness you have done me. May the gods protect you always. Unhappy children, where are you? Come to your father, girls. Ah, how could I have guessed when I, unlucky man, first held you in my arms, that you were born with such a curse upon you? Now I weep bitter tears to think that your lives from here on will be filled with shame and disappointments. If you are happy in good company, it will end with your returning home with tear-filled eyes. And when you reach the age to marry, who will accept the burden of your parents' shame, when he discovers that your father killed his father, then married his own mother, and that the fruits of that unnatural marriage were none other than yourselves? I have one wish to give you, only: that your unlucky destiny may not make your lives as black as your poor father's."

"Enough tears, Oedipus," commanded Creon. "Now go inside."

"I will obey you. Yet no good will come of it for me."

"What does us good is not always what we like, but what we must do when the time arrives."

"I will only go inside on one condition: that you banish me

from this land."

"If that is what the gods desire. But go on, now, and leave your children."

"Do not take them from me!"

"Do not expect to get your own way every time. Remember that everything you won is lost. So go now."

And so two servants guided poor, stumbling Oedipus back into the palace, while the chorus of the elders sent him on his way with these last thoughts:

> *O, Thebans, fellow-countrymen,*
> *Now you have seen it all unfold.*
> *This man who knew, or thought he knew*
> *The answer to riddles none could solve,*
> *And rose to heights of glory and power,*
> *Earning the envy of us all,*
> *Has been storm-lashed and utterly wrecked.*
> *See what fate has befallen him!*
> *Therefore, envy no mortal his luck*
> *Until you have seen how he ends his days.*

OEDIPUS AT COLONUS

after Sophocles

"Antigone, my child, tell me what place we have come to, and if there is anybody here will give help to weary Oedipus, who always gets less than he asks for, yet is content with what little he receives. My sufferings and the burden of my years have taught me patience. If you see some place for me to sit, put me down gently, then let us try to discover where we are and how we may proceed."

"Unlucky father, from what I can make out, there are the walls of some city in the distance. It must be Athens. One thing is sure, though: the spot we are on now is holy ground, for it is filled with flowering laurels and thousand-year-old olive trees, and birds sing sweetly all about, as you can hear. Come, now. Sit here on this stone and rest awhile, for it is a long way still for someone of your age, and I must go and learn what place this is."

"Go, daughter, there should be houses somewhere near."

"There are, father. But no, I do not need to leave you, for there is a man coming our way."

"Yes, I can hear his steps. He's in a hurry."

"He is here already. You can speak to him. He is standing right in front of you."

"I heard you coming, my good man, and my daughter told me, too. She is my eyes, you see. You have arrived at the right moment. Where are we, can you say?"

"Stranger, before you speak another word, get up and leave this place. It is a sacred grove and none should enter it."

"Lead me from here, Antigone," said Oedipus and rose at once. "And you, my man," he went on, "tell us, to which god is this spot consecrated?"

"To fearsome goddesses, daughters of Darkness and mother Earth. Eumenides is our name for them, but in other parts they call them Erinnyes."

"So I have reached the land of the Eumenides. For years I have been wandering, and now at last I have come to the spot where the Fates have promised me release."

"I know nothing of such things, poor fellow, but I will give you any help you need, if it is in my power."

"First tell me the name which this place goes by."

"Colonus, they call it, and it is on the outskirts of Athens. Poseidon and Prometheus the titan hold sway here, but Colonus the horseman is our special protector."

"And who is your ruler – Theseus, perhaps?"

"Yes, the king of Athens."

"And could somebody take him a message from me?"

"Do you wish to beg some favour of him – or would you rather he came here?"

"If he does so, he will profit from it greatly."

"What, profit from a man who cannot see?"

"I, too, was counselled by a blind man when I had my sight, but I did not listen to him."

"Then I shall run to ask our elders concerning what you ask, and if they so decide, it will be done."

"Has the stranger gone, daughter?"

"Yes father, he has left, and now you may speak freely."

"O, immortal Eumenides, O, venerable virgins with your fearsome eyes, do not be harsh, but look with pity on the cruel fate Apollo prophesied so unerringly for me. He even foretold that I would find release in a place where you would give me shelter, and that there my miserable life would come to its end, an end that would benefit those who supported me and bring disaster on those who cast me out. He told me, too, that before my end arrived, I would receive sure signs: an earthquake, thunderclap or a lightning-bolt from Zeus. Something persuades me I would not have found my way here to this grove or seated myself upon your sacred stone if you had not willed it. So now I wait in expectation of your sympathy and help in coming to a quiet end, unless the countless tortures I have suffered are not enough and I must undergo still more. But I believe you will take pity on me, sweet daughters of mother Earth. And you, Athens, holy city with the name and radiance of Pallas Athena, look kindly on this man who was once the renowned Oedipus and is now but his pitiful shadow."

"Hush now, father, for I see some elders coming in search of you."

"Then take me from this place and hide me in the grove. If we hear something, it may tell us what to do."

Antigone had just concealed her father behind the laurels when the search party arrived and Oedipus heard them saying:

"Look over there, search this way and that, until we find who came and set foot in this sacred place."

"There's nobody in sight. Perhaps he is hiding somewhere hereabouts."

"It must be some old beggar. A stranger it'll be, for sure.

No local man would dare to come into the grove of the fearsome virgins whose very name we hesitate to utter."

"We must find him, then. Search everywhere!"

"I am here!" cried Oedipus. "I hear you, but I cannot see, because I have no eyes."

"O Zeus! Who can he be, that old man with the frightful face?"

"I am one whose fate no man on earth would envy. Were it not so, I would not drag myself along with another's eyes to guide me."

"Poor fellow, you look as if some curse has fallen on you."

"As it has, indeed."

"For your own good, listen to us. If you want help, first leave this sacred spot where no human feet may tread, then speak to us."

"Lead me on, then daughter. Reverend elders, I implore you to show sympathy."

"And you shall have it, like every foreigner who is an enemy to what our city hates and who respects the things it loves."

"Tell me, though. Have I come out far enough?"

"Just a few steps more. Come, child, seat him on this stone."

"Take me there, daughter."

"Yes, father. A little bit this way. Now, reach out for the stone, and sit."

"Ah, what a miserable existence!" the luckless Oedipus groaned, as he painfully lowered himself onto the stone.

"Now old man, tell us who you are, your parents' name, and where you come from."

"I am an exile. As for the rest, it is better not to ask me."

"Why? Don't you want to tell us?"

"I am thrice cursed, and scarce know what to say."

"Answer their questions, father. It is not right to hide the truth."

"If that's how things are, I suppose that I must speak. Well, then. Have you heard of Laius' son?"

The searchers recoiled with looks of horror.

"From the line of Labdacus?"

"Ye gods!" they gasped.

"The wretched Oedipus?"

"You are he?"

"Fear not. Whatever evil deeds I was fated to do, I have done already."

"Oh, horrible!"

"All I ask is your pity."

"Leave here at once!"

"Alas!"

"Be gone from our land!"

"And the promises that you gave me?"

"Evil should be repaid with evil. If we show pity on you,

... "You are he?"...

the divine curse will fall on us."

"So I must leave?"

"And quickly, too, lest you delay and worse befall you."

Oedipus stretched out a despairing hand to find his daughter's. She gave it him and he pulled himself to his feet. "Let us be gone," he said, but Antigone did not move. With pain-filled eyes, she looked the elders in the face and said:

"Good strangers, you are kindly men. I see it in your eyes. And if you could hear my old father tell you of the frightful deeds he committed in all innocence, then you would suffer with him. Take pity on me, though, as if I were blood of your blood, and pity him for my sake. You are our only hope, and I implore you by all that you hold sacred, stretch out a helping hand to us. Besides, if the gods are bent on our destruction, then we shall not be saved, whatever help you give us."

"Daughter of Oedipus, we sympathize with you, and with your father, too, for all the great misfortune he has suffered. Yet we fear the anger of the gods and do not dare to aid you."

"So, then," broke in Oedipus, "Athens does not deserve her name as the protector of all strangers! How else can I explain it, when you cast me out for fear of my mere name, and not my deeds? Do not forget that it was through my ignorance I became my own worst victim. So fear the gods now, as you should. They see who shows them true respect and who disdains them. Do not cast me out, I say, for I am here to do good for this land, and if your king comes, he will learn of it. Until he does, be kind to me."

"Wisely spoken, stranger, but they who rule us must decide."

"And your king – where is he?"

"In the palace. But the man who warned us to come here has gone to ask for him."

"Will the king trouble to come all this way for a miserable, blind old man?"

"He will come with all speed when he hears your name."

"But the bearer of the message does not know who I am."

"Fear not. News runs fast from mouth to mouth in this place, and when the king learns who you are, he will fly to your side. You see, old man, your name is known to all, both for your good deeds and for the evil fate you suffered."

Suddenly, Antigone cried: "Ye gods! Who is that I see?"

"What is it daughter?"

"There is a girl coming this way, and she looks like.... No, I cannot believe it! Her head is covered against the sun, but yet I recognize her."

"Who is it, daughter?"

"It is our dear Ismene."

"What did you say, child?"

"I tell you I can see my darling sister. You will recognize her yourself, the moment that you hear her voice."

"Father, dear father! And my own sweet sister!" Ismene cried. "The trouble I have had to find you! Yet how it grieves my heart to see you both like this."

"Dearest daughter, how did you make your way here?"

"Not easily, father. It was a long, slow road – but here I am."

"My child, blood of my blood. Come to my arms!"

"Let me embrace you both at once. Three miserable lives entwined: you father, Antigone and myself the third."

"Ah, daughter, tell me why you came and how you found us."

"It was anxiety for you that brought me here. I have news from the one faithful servant who is left to us in Thebes."

"And why did you have to make the long, tiring journey, and not one of my good-for-nothing sons?"

"Perhaps they will come. Not because they have missed you, though. That is why I had to get here before either of them did."

"Little they care about their father. It is you, my daughters, who bear all the burden. One of you, scarcely out of child-hood, took me by the hand when I was blinded and cast out and led me by rough ways through unknown country, hungry, bare-footed, lashed by tempests and scorched by the fierce sun, giving up all the pleasures of her former life so that her father could have bread to eat. And you, Ismene, if you could

..."My child, blood of my blood. Come to my arms!" ...

but know how much you helped me when, keeping it a secret from the Thebans, you brought me news of all the prophecies concerning wretched Oedipus that were revealed after my banishment. What new message do you bring your father now? What fears for me drove you to venture out into the wilds? I know you would not have taken such a risk unless you bore news of some fresh misfortune."

"I would rather not speak of the trouble I had finding you. It would make the experience doubly painful to retell it. Enough to say that I am here to warn you of the enmity which has flared up between your wretched sons. First of all they quarrelled to gain Creon's favour, since he was governing the country and there was no question of their reigning while the old family curse still hung over them. At last, this envy broke out into open conflict. Who knows whether it was some god drove them to it or just their warped sense of ambition, but they set their hearts on taking back the royal throne. This done, and Creon not contesting it, they agreed to rule for one year each, in turn. However, when his year was up, Eteocles, though younger, refused to hand back power to his brother, and banished him from Thebes. Polyneices then went to Argos and allied himself with king Adrastus by marrying his daughter, and now the two of them have united to make war against our city. These are not mere words, father, but dreadful deeds: brother preparing to do battle against brother. Ah, when will the gods have pity on you?"

"Perhaps the gods may have some pity on me, but as for those two worthless sons of mine, I doubt if they will ever care about their father."

"Yet now the time has come when, with false words of love, they will try to persuade you it is otherwise. Oracles have revealed that whichever of them fails to get you back to Thebes will lose. You can expect Creon to be here before long, to curry favour with you and beg you to return."

"I could forgive him for worse things, if only I knew that when I died, sweet Theban earth would cover me."

"That is something neither brother wants. When I said Thebes, I meant close by, but not within its borders. They still consider you an evil influence, father, though one they are both eager to profit from."

"So they will take me away from here, the wretches, putting the throne and their deadly hatred above the love they owe me. Since that is all they want, my curse upon them! May the gods hunt them down, and may the furious enmity which sets them at each other's throats turn and destroy them both! May he who now reigns lose the throne, and the other never gain it! Ungrateful sons! When the madness was upon me and I longed to die or be stoned by the people, they gave me no comfort in my misery. And when in time my troubled mind found rest and I realised what revenge my anger had driven me to take upon myself, then they abandoned me without a pang of conscience. My own sons, who could have saved me with a single word, let their blind father be sent out into lonely exile, to be lashed by cruel storms. My daughters, on the other hand, though weak, shared in my sorrows and did not let me wander groping in the darkness. They gave that helping hand a child owes to its parents. But my sons? Oh, no! They preferred warring for a throne and sceptre to coming to their father's aid! No, they shall never have my backing in their foul ambitions, let them send Creon or whoever else they choose to call for me. I shall go with no one. And so, kind strangers, I beg of you and of the goddesses who guard your land to stand beside me in the certain knowledge that from your help great good will come to your city, just as great evil will fall upon my enemies."

"You deserve our pity, Oedipus, and we have some advice to give you."

"I will do whatever you suggest."

"If you seek the help of the Eumenides, our goddesses, you must make the proper sacrifices at their altar. If you cannot do this with your own hands, then one of your daughters must perform the rites. If all is done exactly as it should be, it will enable us to help you without fear."

"Do you hear what these kind people counsel us, my children? I have neither strength nor eyes to guide me, so one of you must do it in my place."

"I will go, father," Ismene offered willingly, "but you must tell me where the altar is and exactly what I have to do."

"Go over there, beyond the grove," one of the elders told her, "and you will find a man who will explain it all to you."

"Very well, then. You, Antigone, watch over our father. It is no burden to put oneself out for a parent." And with these words she hurried off to do her duty.

"Stranger, although I do not wish to open up old wounds," said the first among the elders, "I long to know how you fell into this miserable state. Your misfortunes are much talked about, but stories vary, and I would like to hear the tale from your own lips."

"No man ever came into this world with a birthright more terrible than mine – but why must you remind me of my horrible sufferings?"

"Yet tell me, for I have told you everything you wanted."

"I was made to sin without my knowledge, when the city bound me in an unholy marriage."

"With your own mother?"

"It cuts me like a knife to hear it. But what are these poor girls of mine to blame if they were born of the same mother as myself?"

"Daughters, yet sisters of their father, too. That is horrible and unheard-of. How did it come about?"

"Because I was given the queen of Thebes as a prize – a prize I wish I had never claimed!"

"I have heard another terrible thing, too. They say you killed your father."

"Another stab in the same wound. One that hurts more keenly because I was not to blame. I did not know it was he, and besides, I was fighting for my life."

"You are to be pitied, you poor, luckless man. But we have said enough, for here comes Theseus, our king. You begged to see him, and he has hurried here to meet you."

"Unfortunate Oedipus," said Theseus, "your ruined eye-sockets tell me who you are. I came because I knew you would not have asked for me without a serious reason. I, too, grew up far from home and endured terrible dangers in inhospitable lands, and that is why I always lend a helping hand to strangers. I, too, am mortal, and never know what the next day may bring."

"Noble Theseus, I thank you for your kindly words. Since you have realised who I am and where I come from, there is nothing more for me to tell you but what it is that brings me here."

"I am listening, poor Oedipus."

"I have a gift to offer you. It is only my miserable body, and yet one day it will bring you great good fortune. When that day will come, however, is something you shall not find out until the proper time."

"How will you make this offering to me?"

"By dying. You will give me a final resting-place and I shall give you something of great value in return."

"But I would do this thing you ask of me in any case. It is our duty to do honour to the dead."

"In my case, it may not prove easy. You may have to fight to secure an end for Oedipus in this land."

"Who do you fear, then? Is it your sons, perhaps?"

"You have guessed rightly. They will try to take me off by force."

"Surely it is better to live in your own country than in exile?"

"Yet when I wanted to go on living in my home, they would not let me stay."

"Yes, but it serves no purpose to go on holding that against them."

"Give me your advice, then. But first hear me out."

"Very well. Explain yourself."

"I have been struck by one blow upon another. The last was when my own sons cast me out as a father-killer."

"If they did that, why do they want you back again?"

"An oracle has forced them to it. But there is another prophecy which foretells they will be defeated at your hands."

"Why me? There is no enmity between us."

"Dear son of Aegeus, one thing in this world is sure: the gods will never know old age or death. All else, the mighty hand of time turns upside-down. With its passing, the rich earth turns to desert and the strong, lithe body withers. Faith becomes faint and the unbeliever flourishes. The winds of change blow cold and turn friends and cities upon one another. Although you are at peace with Thebes today, time could ruffle those smooth waters with its passing, and some petty disagreement may prove enough for you to arm yourselves for war against each other. As sure as Zeus is Zeus and Apollo his true prophet, I tell you that those who scorn the gods today will be destroyed tomorrow. Only hold true to the word you gave me, and if the gods are not deceiving me, you will have no cause to regret it."

"I never go back on my word, above all when I have given it to a man who comes as a suppliant to our altars and makes such an offer to our city. And now if you have no objection, I would like you to come and stay with me in Athens."

"I would dearly love to do so, but I must stay here and face the ones who cast me out. I will need your help in this – but take care, for they will use threats of force to gain their ends."

"My heart does not know fear. No one shall succeed in taking you from me by violence. Let them but try, and they will soon repent of it. My name alone is sufficient to protect you. I will leave you now. Since I have come to Colonus, I must make an offering at Poseidon's altar." With these words, Theseus walked off, while the chorus of the elders broke into song:

> *Stranger, you've come to a wonderful place.*
> *There is no lovelier in the world.*
> *For nowhere but Colonus will you hear*
> *The nightingale sing in tones so sweet*
> *Hidden among the glossy leaves*
> *Of the ivy-tod in the sacred grove,*
> *The untrodden place where no winds rage*
> *In the depths of winter, no shadows move*
> *As Bacchus sleeps off his drunken feast*
> *In the solitude of sweet quietness.*

> *Here, each morning, the narcissus flowers,*
> *Bathed in dewdrops; and crocus, pale-gold,*
> *Weaves fragrant crowns for the goddesses.*
> *And the river Cephissus' waters clear*
> *Which make our green fields their fruits to bear*
> *Never cease murmuring their sweet song.*
> *And the muses listen with bated breath*
> *While Aphrodite, the golden one,*
> *Bestows her gift of love on the world.*

Here stranger, there grows the envied tree
Whose fruit is the food of intrepid men,
Whose oil gives light in the dark of night
And whose branches are symbols in praise of peace.
Though the olive tree with its grey-green leaves
Be regarded with envy in the west
And seen by the east with a jealous eye,
Neither east nor west would dare do it harm,
For Athena and Zeus keep watch over it.

There are other things that our proud land boasts:
Our steeds and our ships are both unmatched.
Ours was the stallion whose hot pride
Poseidon the son of Cronus broke,
Here in our flowering meadows, when
He first put bridle upon a horse.
It was he first carved the broad-bladed oar,
Gave wings to our ships, and showed our crews
How to beat the wine-dark sea into foam,
Speeding faster across the waves
Than the fifty daughters of old Nereus.

"A land to be envied, indeed!" sighed Antigone. "But now the time has come, I see, when it must prove its worth to us as well."

"Why do you say that? Is anything amiss?" asked Oedipus.

"Creon is coming, father. He has a band of men with him, and I am scared."

"Oh, elders, who will save me now?" cried Oedipus.

"Do not trouble your mind with that. We may be old, but know that in this land, strength has not yet grown feeble."

Soon Creon stood before them.

"Good citizens of this country," he said gently, "I see something like fear in your eyes, perhaps because I have arrived so unexpectedly. I am not here for any evil purpose, though. Indeed an old man like myself would never dream of coming to a peerless city such as Athens with wicked aims in mind. I am only here to make this luckless man come home to Thebes, now that we all want him back again: his people, his son Eteocles who rules the city and I, his relative, who cannot bear to hear of him wandering in foreign lands. I pity his unfortunate daughter, too. She has lost everything for her father's sake, including any hope of gaining a husband and children, and risks being carried off by some lustful villain. So, Oedipus, although you cannot see, turn your face towards me and listen to what I have to say to you. Let bygones be bygones and allow me to take you back to your ancestral palace, and to the homeland whose worth you should respect and whose wishes you should hasten to obey."

"Creon, I know very well why you want me, and what my fate will be if I go with you. You speak fair words, but they ring false, and I will not fall into the trap which you and my faithless son have set for me. Truly, how do you explain this sudden pity for me? When I longed for you to banish me you would not do it, but the moment my mad ravings calmed and I begged to be allowed to stay, you cast me out. A relative of mine, you call yourself. What kind of relative were you to me then? I know that all the city wants me, and always has done, but not you or that son. I say out loud, for everyone to hear, that you fear to bring me into Thebes, but wish to keep me penned up just beyond its borders. That will not happen, Creon. You will not go back with Oedipus, but you will take his curse back with you, a curse I throw at both that son who is your ally, and the other who is preparing to make war against you. I know what territory each of them will gain in Thebes – enough, and just enough to hold their corpses! You see I am better informed than you about the future, because I get my news from wiser mouths than yours, from Zeus and from his son Apollo. So, be gone, and let me not waste further words on you, since I would a thousand times prefer to live my days out in a foreign land than come back with you to Thebes."

"Alas, it seems that neither years nor bitter experience have taught you your own good, and you prefer an old age filled with shame to the honours which we offer you."

"You have a clever tongue, but do not hope to snare me."

"Some talk in torrents, while others only say what's necessary."

"He who counts his words does so to see how he will profit by them."

"No man can count his words when he has lost his wits."

"Will you be gone, at last? Nobody wants you here."

"I shall not go until I have achieved my purpose."

"Do not think you will be able to take me from this place by force. I have trusty friends here, and strong ones, too."

"Yet you will soon be weeping bitter tears."

"You crafty villain! Do you threaten me with something fearful?"

"With your daughters. I have already laid my hands on one of them, because I knew the kind of stubborn resistance I would meet. My men are holding her."

"God help me!"

"Yes, bitter tears I said, and soon you will be weeping harder still, when I snatch the other from you."

"My friends, the hour has come for me to seek your help. Hold to the word you gave me, and chase this false-hearted villain from your land!"

"Leave, stranger! You have abused the hospitality of a welcoming land, and piled foul deeds upon false words."

"I shall not leave unless I take her with me."

"Oh, father, woe is me! They are dragging me away!"

"Give me your hand, my child! Daughter, where are you? Elders of the land, where have you gone? Why do you let him get away with this?"

"Fear not, we are at your side. So, stranger, you have come to rob us! Let her go this instant!"

"I am holding nothing that is not mine by right. I am only taking back my own."

"Then you shall see our strength!"

"Stand back!"

"Onto him, citizens!"

"Touch me and you shall have war!"

"Then give us the girl."

"Keep your orders for those that you have power over!"

"Release the girl, do you hear?"

"Get back, I tell you!"

"Quickly, friends! Come quickly! Our city is being put to shame by this man's insolence. Run! Run!"

"Father, save me!" cried Antigone in despair.

"Come to me, my child!"

"I cannot. They are dragging me away."

"Carry her off. Take her with the other one!" commanded Creon.

"This is too much to bear!" groaned Oedipus.

"Now you no longer have your girls to guide you – and

... "Daughter, where are you?"...

whose fault is it but your own, since you chose to put yourself above your homeland and your people. This stubbornness of yours will cost you dearly yet."

"What worse fate could I suffer?"

"To be carried off yourself!"

"That, never!" cried the elders. "You will pay for everything you've done!"

"Why, do you think I am afraid of this pitiful old man?"

"Yes, you should fear me, for I still have some power left. If the gods do not deprive me of my voice, I shall curse you, villain, for carrying off these girls of mine who were my eyes. May the all-seeing Helios afflict you with a miserable old age like mine!"

"Listen to him, the foul-mouthed beggar!" cried Creon to the elders.

"They hear, and see, and judge – of that you can be sure. Your deeds speak for themselves."

"You have driven me too far! I shall drag you off with my own hands! Don't think I am too old for it!"

"Alas, what more must I suffer?"

"No harm will come to you," the elders reassured him. "Such brazen insolence does not go unpunished in this land."

"I shall do what I have to," insisted Creon.

"As long as Athens can call herself a free city, you will not lay a finger on this man."

"He who has justice on his side can defeat the most powerful of adversaries, for Zeus is his protector."

"Your words are blasphemy, when you seek the help of Zeus in such a task."

"Whatever they may be, you have no choice but to accept them. See! Here come my men."

"Come quickly, men of Colonus!" the elders cried. "Run, masters, run! Help us to save this poor old man! Come quickly!"

Theseus himself was first to arrive in answer to the elders' shouts.

"What is going on here?" he demanded. "Your cries alarmed me, and I left the sacrifice and came. Tell me now – what is happening?"

"This man has done me a hideous injustice," Oedipus protested.

"Who is he – and what is it he's done to you?"

"He is Creon of Thebes, and he has robbed me of my only support – my daughters."

"What did you say?"

"Exactly what you heard."

"Then we must lose no time. Send someone to the altar straight away to warn my men. Tell them I command they leave the sacrifice and ride at top speed for the road to Thebes. They must catch the fellows who have carried off the girls

before they get away and shame me in the eyes of this man
who has come to our land seeking help. As for you, stranger,
I prefer to hold my wrath in check, or else you might not
leave my hands alive. Do not imagine, though, that I will let
you go your way unless you bring me back the girls, for you
have insulted both me and our city's hospitality. Perhaps you
thought that there were no brave men in Athens, and I was
someone not worth reckoning with. If so, you were mistaken,
and you will earn no praise from Thebes when it is learned
how you have trampled on the holy laws by carrying off those
who came seeking refuge, and shamed your city in the act. I
said it before and I will say it once again: someone must bring
them back or you will remain here as a prisoner."

"Son of Aegeus, you do me an injustice if you think I do
not hold your city in the esteem which she deserves. On the
contrary, I only have her interests at heart, for I believe that
Athens would be put to shame if she sank as low as to give
refuge to my countrymen against my will. Above all she would
never wish to harbour one so loathed by gods and mortals, a
man who killed his father, then married his own mother and
spawned tainted children on her. I am convinced of all these
things because I know that you respect the judgements of your
supreme council which meets upon the hill of Ares, and that
no vile sinner who reeks of murderous incest would be per-
mitted to defile your land. That is why I seized the girls, and

... "What is going on here?" demanded Theseus...

even then I would have left them had their insolence not provoked me beyond measure, for rage knows nothing of old
age and only fades with death. This is what I had to tell you.
Now do what you will, for I am in your hands – but if you use
violence against me, I shall reply with violence, old though I
am."

Creon's words spurred Oedipus to a furious retort.

"Have you no shame?" he cried. "Who do you think you
blacken with your words, me or yourself? You speak of murder, marriage, and the misery I suffered, but you do not say I
did these things in ignorance, and only because the gods so
willed it in their rage against my family, before I ever came
into the world. Can you accuse me of knowingly preferring
lawlessness to honest deeds? If I killed my father, it was because I was driven to it by the gods, when I was fleeing my
country to avoid that very thing. As for my marriage with my
mother, villain, you should be the last to mention it, since she
was your own sister and you know better than any man on
earth that neither she nor I could ever in our wildest imaginings
have guessed I was her son. But no, you take delight in throwing these things in my face, because you know the bitter pain
it causes me to hear them, while if you felt for me, you would
stay silent. And at the same time you so shamelessly accuse
me, you voice your hypocritical praise of Athens, believing it
will help you to achieve your lawless aim. Wrong! if there is

any city which respects the ruling of the gods, it is the one whose guest you have tried to carry off, and whose daughters you have already laid your hands upon. So now I kneel before the goddesses of this land and beg them to let you taste the keen edge of their sword."

Moved by Oedipus' impassioned words, the elders turned to Theseus and said:

"This poor, defenceless stranger deserves all the help that we can give him, your majesty."

"And quickly, too," responded Theseus, "for we are losing time. The kidnappers are getting away while we stand here with folded arms and let them take advantage of us."

"And what of me?" asked Creon. "I am your prisoner. What do you command?"

"First tell me where the girls are. Even if your men have ridden off with them, they will not have time to thank the gods for their escape. My own men will be waiting for them on the road. Just come with me and do exactly what I tell you. You may have trapped two innocent creatures, but now you're tangled in your own nets, and it's time for you to learn that you cannot profit from ill-gotten gains. Do not hope for rescue, either. However strong the forces you have brought, I am prepared for them. I think we understand each other, unless you take my words as lightly as you planned this little escapade."

"I do not blame you for speaking to me thus. But I warn you, Thebes will not take this lying down."

"Threaten me to your heart's content, but come this way. And you, dear Oedipus, wait here. Be sure that if I am not doomed to die in this encounter, I will return, and with your children."

"Go with my blessing, noble Theseus. I thank you for supporting my just cause."

They left, and once more the chorus of the elders broke into song.

Oh, to be there when they face the abductors
And the battlefield echoes with clashing of arms!
Will it be at the pass, where the Sacred Way narrows,
Or down on the sea shore, where the two goddesses,
Mother and daughter, stand by the torch-bearers
At solemn festivals? Somewhere down there, it seems,
With paeans of victory, our great leader Theseus
Will snatch Oedipus' daughters from Thebes' lawless
       hands.

But perhaps they have taken the road through the forest
And are galloping now on their swift-footed steeds
Beneath the white flanks of the snow-covered hills
Beyond where the shepherds graze flocks on Mount Oia.

But they shall not escape! For the ardour of Theseus
And the young men of Athens cannot be contained
As they lunge on their chargers and honour Athena,
Most brilliant of riders, and the sea-god Poseidon.

Has the skirmish begun? Ah, a voice seems to cry
That Zeus will grant Athens the victory today
And the poor maidens' terrors will soon have an end.
Oh, for the wings of a swift-flying dove,
To soar into the sky and look down from on high
As the lawless are crushed by the virtuous and brave!

Oh, almighty Zeus from whom nothing is hidden
Stand by our men, who have right on their side!
And you, virgin goddess, Pallas Athena,
Daughter of Zeus, go swiftly in search
Of Apollo the archer and straight-shooting Artemis,
And with bow, sword and spear, hasten all of you there
Where the brave take up arms for the laws of the gods.

Just as the chorus was ending, Theseus returned with Oedipus' two daughters.

"Father! Oh, father!" They both cried together.

"My children, is it really you?"

"Thanks to this worthy man and his brave soldiers," replied Antigone, as she and Ismene fell into their father's open arms. And he, poor man, said, weeping tears of joy:

"All that I hold dear in the world I clasp in my embrace, and if death takes me now, it will find me a happy man. Hug me tight, and soothe the pains which torture my mind. I can hardly believe you are both here safe and sound. How did it come about?"

"The man who saved us is here, father. He is the king of Athens, and he will tell you everything you want to know."

"O Theseus, worthy ruler of a worthy city, may the gods pour their blessings on both you and your people. All I have left in the world, I owe to you, for nowhere else have I found such devotion to the holy laws, such sympathy for my misery and such hatred of all falsehood. How was the faithless Creon defeated? Tell me, so that my soul may rejoice."

"I thank you for your kind words, Oedipus. You have your daughters now, and how I won the battle is of no importance. What matters is that I did not prove false to the vow I swore to you. Now there is something else I wish to tell you. I have learned that a relative of yours has come here to beg a favour at the altar of Poseidon."

"Who can he be, and what does he want of the god – or is there something that he wants from me, perhaps?"

"They say that he wants you to agree to listen to him, so that he can seek a promise from you."

... "The man who saved us is here"...

"But what kind of promise can that be, if he asks the god Poseidon first, instead of coming straight to me? Who is this man and where has he come from? Doesn't anyone know anything?

"He is someone who has come from Argos. Do you have any relation there who might want to beg some favour from you?"

"From Argos? A favour? Enough. Let us speak of other things."

"Why, what is wrong?"

"Do not ask me."

"Will you not tell me?"

"I know that the person who has come is someone I neither wish to meet nor hear."

"But if that is the case, all the more reason to tell me, your friend, who this man is."

"He is the son I loathe, Polyneices, and I could endure no greater evil than to hear his voice and to know that he was standing before my ruined eyes."

"But why? No harm can come of receiving him and hearing what he has to say, since nothing can oblige you to do what he requests."

"Because I hate the very sound of his voice. It is only now that he remembers that he has a father, and then merely out of self-interest. That is why I beg you not to ask me to relent."

"I would not ask you such a thing; indeed, I would not even recommend it, had he not come to Poseidon's altar to seek aid. As things are, it would not be right to turn him away without a hearing."

Here Antigone broke in. "Father," she reminded Oedipus, "in our misery, there were many times when you turned to me for advice, in spite of my tender years. So I shall give you my opinion now. You must heed the words of this king who has given us so much help. Let my brother come here and be heard by you. You cannot be made to change your mind by force, if you do not like what you hear, and merely listening to him will cost you nothing. Besides, whatever harm he may have done you, you should not repay him in the same coin, for after all, he is your son. Let him come, father. Other parents have been angered by their children's heartlessness, but they allowed the advice of friends to soften them. You suffered many evils at the hands of your own parents. Do not forget that, for rage kept burning fierce ends badly. Relent, I say, for it is not right to make these people beg you to agree to something which is logical and just. Besides, they have been kind to us, and you should not accept that kindness and then ignore their kindly-meant opinion."

"Antigone, my child, what more can I say? Your words have won me over. Let him come, then. But he must be satisfied with my answer, and no one else's."

"But that is as it should be," replied Theseus. "And let me add, though I am not a man to boast, that there is no man you need fear, as long as the gods grant me my strength."

"But here he comes!" cried Antigone.

"Who are you talking about?"

"The person we were speaking of. Polyneices has arrived, and he is standing before you now."

"Ah, what do I see, sisters?" Polyneices cried. "Instead of bewailing my own fate, the time has come for me to weep for our old father. Here he stands, exiled and defenceless, dirty and tousle-haired, his clothes tattered and unwashed, and worst of all, he is nothing but a bag of skin and bones. Too late I see these things, and shame on me, for I, too, am to blame for the sufferings he has endured. I must be the worst man in the world, for I did not spare a single thought for my own father. Yet may the spirit of kindness which stands at Zeus' right hand and gives him her advice, look kindly on me now that I feel remorse for my hard-heartedness. Father, why do you turn your head aside? Will you not say a single word to me? Will you not even tell me why you are so angry? Ah, sisters, speak to him yourselves, beg him to open his mouth and not dismiss me from his presence in disgrace, since I have prayed for help at the altar of Poseidon."

"If you are so anxious to hear his voice," replied Antigone, "then tell him why you are here and what you want. Whether he is pleased or furious, he will feel the need to answer you."

"You are right, sister. I will tell him everything. But first I wish to call upon the aid of the god at whose altar I knelt down, and to thank the king of this country, who gave me permission to journey here, to speak and to be heard, and then to leave unharmed. Now, father, I shall tell you the reason I have come to you. As you may know, I was exiled from my homeland because I sought the royal power which belongs to me by right, being the eldest of your sons. But Eteocles dethroned me without any justification, without a struggle and without a victory, choosing instead to deceive our people with his lies. Exiled, I went to Argos, where I married the daughter of king Adrastus. In that city, I formed bonds of friendship with various gallant warlords who offered to help me to win back my throne. Now, with seven armies and seven generals at their heads, we have set out to lay siege to Thebes, having first sworn a solemn oath to unseat those who wronged me, or to die in the attempt. Father, I have come to ask a favour for myself and for my allies. You know them all: first there is Adrastus, then Tydeus of Calydon, third Amphiaraus, the matchless spearsman and great seer. The fourth is Hippomedon, sent by his father Talaus, and next comes Capaneus, who boasts that he can knock the walls of Thebes down with his own bare hands. The sixth is Parthenopaeus the Arcadian, the worthy son of Atalanta, while I, that fruit of evil fortune who calls himself your son, make up the seven. All of us, father, beg you by everything that you hold sacred, and on the lives of your beloved daughters, to set aside the anger you have every right to feel against me. For now I am setting off for war to avenge myself upon the brother who cast me out and snatched the throne that was mine by right of birth. I have come to seek your support, for if the holy oracles of Apollo are to be believed, victory will fall to whichever of the two of us has his father at his side. This is why I beg you by the sacred streams of your ancestral lands and by all our household gods, to lay your heavy anger to one side and agree to come with me. For I am poor and exiled, just as you, and like you I am fated to live as a suppliant, cultivating the good will of others, while Eteocles has everything, and sits in smug security upon the throne he stole from me. Yet I shall crush the wretch if you but give me your blessing and come over to my side; and then, father, I will bring you back home to the palace, where you can stay with me and forget all the misery you have endured in foreign lands. I promise you all this, and I pride myself that I will keep my word if this should be your will. If not, then all is lost for both of us."

Polyneices now waited with bated breath for his father's answer. But Oedipus stood there and uttered not a word. Finally, the leader of the elders broke the silence:

"Give the man an answer, my good lord. If not for his sake,

at least for the sake of king Theseus, who allowed him to come here. Give him the answer you see fit, then let him go on his way."

"Dear friends, had it not been Theseus who sent him to me, he would never have heard the sound of my voice. But now he will hear such words that he will never know a moment's joy again. Miserable hypocrite! When your word passed for law in Thebes, was it not you who ordered your own father to be banished with nothing but the clothes I stood in, not caring if I became a homeless wanderer? You see me now, and the tears come to your eyes – not because you have any feeling for me, but only since you have fallen on hard times yourself. Do you think I want such tears? I know who cast me out into the street like any common beggar. I know that I would not be living now if I did not have the help and comfort of my daughters, who bear their burden for me as well as any man could do. Be gone, I say. Take yourself off to the place where fate has ruled that you will pay for your impiety. For if indeed your armies ever set out against Thebes, then mark my words, you will never put a foot inside the city. You and your brother will die as fortune has ordained, and your hands will be stained with each other's blood. Was it my blessing that you sought? I give my curse instead – on both of you, to teach you as you make your way to Hades that a father is to be respected, not scorned when he is blind and helpless. And remember this – you and all those like you – whether you kneel in supplication at the altar or preen yourselves on some high throne, divine justice holds you in her hand, she who keeps unsleeping watch upon the unwritten laws of Zeus. My curse on you, I say, and may Apollo's prophecy prove true. May you live neither to set foot on the sacred soil of Thebes nor to go back to Argos, but die upon your brother's sword in the very moment that you kill him. At least you will die in each other's arms that way, though you never shared a brotherly embrace when you were living. Did you hear me? Be on your way now, and pass the message to your followers. Shout it out loud to the Thebans, too, so all may learn that Oedipus has shared his inheritance equally between his sons!"

"Alas, alas, Polyneices," groaned the elders. "You came to beg a favour and leave worse than empty-handed. Now there is nothing left for you to do but pursue the path that leads onward to your doom."

"So it means disaster, then, for me and for my allies. Was it for such an evil end as this that we set out from Argos? Yet I cannot tell a soul that we are doomed to lose our lives before the seven gates of Thebes. Now, sisters, in the name of all the gods I beg you, if our father's curse should work on me, and you ever happen to come home, do not deny this favour to me: bury my miserable body with all the honours fitting to the dead, so that my soul may not roam miserably

... "My curse on you, I say"...

for all eternity. And if they praise you now for the burden you have taken on in caring for my father, you will earn praise warmer still if you do that thing for me."

"Polyneices, if you value your life, then listen to me."

"What do you wish to tell me, Antigone?"

"Lead your army back to Argos."

"That is impossible. I will not be called a deserter and a coward."

"But what will you gain, if you destroy your own city and lose your life along with it?"

"And what is there to lose, if I must live in exile while my brother laughs at my expense?"

"So you prefer to kill each other and let the prophecy come true?"

"No prophecy will make me change my mind."

"You will see things in a different light when your allies all desert you; for who will dare to follow in your steps when they learn the oracles foretell your downfall?"

"I will make sure they never learn of them. A general who knows his job announces all the good news and keeps back the bad."

"Are you so determined, then?"

"I am, so do not try to hold me any longer. I shall pursue my course, though it leads to my destruction. My father and the fates have willed it on me. That is all I have to say – and now good-bye. If you have any love for me, dear sisters, all you can do is take care of me when I am dead, for this is the last time you will see me in this life."

"Alas, alas! Our poor brother is running straight into the mouth of Hades."

Now Polyneices was gone, and once again the chorus of the elders spoke:

> *Again, bad news to make us groan,*
> *Yet since the fates desire it so,*
> *It is not our place to defy their will.*
> *And who can make a stand against*
> *The strength of the immortal gods,*
> *Whose decrees have never gone unobeyed?*
> *With the passage of time, much foretold comes to pass,*
> *In a single day, many things are laid low*
> *And new things raised up in the heaven above.*
>
> *O Zeus, the sky is lit up by your bolts!*
> *The ground is shaken by thunder-claps.*
> *Darkness envelops us like a shroud.*
> *What is the message you send, O god?*

"The message is for me, for Oedipus. Let us hurry. Some-one must run to bring king Theseus."

The sky is riven by crashing fire!
How can such chaos bode well for us?
Ah, once more the lightning strikes fear in our hearts!
How will your anger end, O Zeus?
Father of men, if by chance we have erred
And given shelter to someone you hate,
Then we fall before you on bended knee
And beg you to turn your wrath from us.

"Theseus! Where is Theseus? He must reach me while I am still living. I owe him a great debt for all that he has done for me."

King of Athens, thrice glorious,
Wherever you are, come now in haste.
The stranger is calling you and he wants
To repay the kindness you showed to him
With gifts for the city, his friends and you.
Do not delay, for the river in flood
Can never return to its source; and time,
Which pities no man, surges on unmoved,
Sweeping all in its path. So, Theseus, hurry
– For the stranger, the city, his friends and yourself.

Within moments, Theseus was at their side.

"Elders, Why did you call for me?" he asked. "You, Oedipus, what do you want of me? And why has Zeus sent all this thunder and lightning? What can it mean?"

"It means my end has come, Theseus. The gods, who do not know what it is to lie, have sent me word that through these thunderclaps and bolts of lightning I shall walk forward to my destiny."

"I believe you, Oedipus, for all the gods have told you so far has proved true. Only tell me what part I must play in this."

"I will. Before I die, I shall reveal to you a secret that will be a blessing to your city today, tomorrow and for all eternity. Though I am blind, I shall now walk on alone, without a guide, to the place where I must die. You shall follow in my footsteps, with my daughters some way behind you. But only you will learn where and how Oedipus met his end, and of that you will never say a word to anyone. You alone will hear the secret which shall bring your city more good fortune than any earthly power could ever bestow upon it. You will keep that secret as a sacred trust, and only when your death approaches will you reveal it to the man who shall succeed you. He in his turn will pass it with his dying breath to the ruler who ascends his throne. Now follow me, and do not be anxious lest I lose my footing, for I shall be guided by Hermes, leader of dead souls, and Persephone who reigns in Hades."

So Oedipus walked on, followed by Theseus and the two girls, until he reached the place where an oath of friendship between Theseus and Perithous was cut into the rock. Near it was an opening in the ground which led into the mouth of Hades. Then Oedipus asked his daughters to bathe him, as was the custom with the dead. The moment this rite was performed, there was a deafening clap of thunder, and the girls threw themselves to the ground in terror, clutching their father's legs and kissing them.

"My children," said Oedipus, "from this day on, you will no longer have the father whom you loved so much and cared for, and who loved you in return above all daughters in the world. Now you will go forth into life alone, but relieved of the heavy burden of attending to my daily needs. Nor will you need to trouble yourselves about my burial, for the gods who have pursued me so relentlessly have at last shown mercy, and I am bidden to go down into Hades as I am, without enduring the bitter throes of death."

With these words, he gathered them into his arms, and the three of them stood locked in tight embrace, shaken by sobs.

Then a hollow voice was heard, echoing from deep beneath the opening in the earth:

"Oedipus! Why are you waiting still? The hour has come, and you delay."

Oedipus knew who was calling, and he beckoned Theseus to his side.

"I entrust my daughters to you, Theseus," he said. "I know that you will do what's best for them. And you, my orphaned children, be brave and bid farewell to your father now, lest you see things which are not meant for your eyes, or hear what only the king of Athens must be told."

Their eyes brimming with tears, the two girls did his bidding and withdrew. Then Oedipus took Theseus by the hand, and the two of them walked steadily on towards the dark cleft in the rock.

Soon Theseus returned, alone, both joy and sadness written on his face: joy at the secret which Oedipus had entrusted to him, but bitter sadness at the loss of that brave heart. When he reached the girls, he said:

"Your father's life was one long, bitter torment, but he left this world relieved of all the hideous guilt which weighed upon his soul, and with my promise that I would do whatever lies within my power for you. Do not weep now, for the death the gods have granted to king Oedipus is an honour no man on earth has ever yet received. Your father walked down into Hades on his own two feet, leaving no grave nor any need for mourning."

Cheered by Theseus' words, the two girls wiped away their tears, and Antigone said:

"The greatest favour you can do for us is to get us back to Thebes as soon as possible. Perhaps there is still time to avert the doom which hangs over our brothers' heads."

"I shall do that and whatever else you may desire, for your sakes, and for the debt I owe to a man who, if he sinned, did so in such a way that mankind will do him honours till the end of time."

THE SEVEN AGAINST THEBES

Freely based on Euripides' "Phoenisses"
and Aeschylus' "Epta epi Thivas"

Outside the palace gate at Thebes, Antigone was waiting anxiously for the arrival of her faithful tutor. She had given him secret instructions to find his way into the camp of the seven warlords who now held the city under siege, to try to gain an audience with Polyneices and persuade him to parley with Eteocles, in the hope that some good might come of the meeting and a bloody contest between the two brothers be averted. At last her old teacher appeared.

"Over here," she cried, and as the tutor drew nearer, she asked him anxiously, "Tell me, did you see my brother?"

"I did, and he accepted your proposal. He will come to find you, and he has no objection to meeting with Eteocles."

"I cannot tell you how happy that news makes me, dear old friend. But tell me, does he not fear to come alone into the city?"

"He is well aware of the danger, but he tells me that for your sake it is a risk he is prepared to take."

"For my sake only? Does he not wish to settle his differences with his brother in a peaceful way?"

"Well, yes and no. He wants to talk, yet he loathes Eteocles and says he will not let him keep a throne which is not his by right."

"In other words, if Eteocles does not back down, blood will be shed?"

"I fear so. As we spoke, he kept glancing at his allies, the Argive chieftains, and I knew that in their steely eyes he could read their eagerness to hurl themselves upon the walls, break down the city gates and bring Thebes to her knees, drowning all resistance in our blood. It is too late now for Polyneices to go back on his word. Ignoring all the dangers, he must steal into the city and meet with Eteocles in your presence, although he professes to have little hope that his brother will see reason and give up the crown. When the other leaders heard what he intended, they made their disagreement clear. 'We have Thebes in our hands already,' they protested. 'Booty by the pile, and slaves without number.' If you had heard their voices and seen the greed gleam in their eyes, you'd have said Thebes' days were numbered."

"And does Polyneices go along with this?"

"Ah, child, you must realise that of all the evils that have wormed their way into the palaces of kings, the worst is lust for power. It sets brother against brother, father against his children, and those same children at their father's throat. Now that same lust has blinded your two brothers. Just climb these steps and you will see with your own eyes. From up there, all their camp is visible. When you see the work that's going on, you will understand they have no thought of withdrawal."

"Yes, I would like to do that. Call it concern, or merely idle curiosity, but I want to see what is happening beneath our walls. Give me your hand a moment."

"Here, but be careful how you climb."

"I will, old friend. Just look at them! Ah, brothers, what god has goaded you into this fratricidal war? Why, oh why?"

"To fulfil the curse of Pelops and drown the house of Labdacus in blood. But come, see over there. They are setting out the troops in companies, and the Argive army is taking up position."

"I am afraid, my dear old friend. Why, the whole plain is

glittering with their weapons!"

"Do not imagine Polyneices would set off without first making careful preparations. That is why I tell you there is no longer any margin for retreat. But tell me, can you make out any of the leaders?"

"Yes, that one with the white crest on his helmet, who is standing in the front. Who can he be, I wonder?"

"That is Hippomedon of Mycenae. A valiant warlord."

"He looks like a savage giant to me. I tremble just to look at him."

"More fearsome still is that one with the strangely-decorated armour. He is Tydeus of Calydon."

"You mean the one who married the sister of Polyneices' wife?"

"And who now threatens all Thebes with destruction? Yes, I do."

"Alas, my brother has married into evil company. But say, who is that walking past the tomb of Zethus? He must be a general of some kind – so many troops are following him."

"That is Parthenopaeus, the son of Atalanta."

"Ah, If only Artemis had shot him with one of her keen arrows, when she was hunting with his mother on the mountainside, instead of letting him live to do my city harm!"

"Yes, if only she had – but the gods have other plans."

"Plans for our destruction, no doubt. But tell me, where is

my brother? Can you see Polyneices?"

"Down there, by the tomb of the seven daughters of Niobe. Next to him is standing Adrastus, his father-in-law and king of Argos."

"Ah, yes, I see them both. Yet how can my brother wish Thebes any harm? The moment he comes, I will fall down at his feet and beg him to forget the ill treatment he has suffered, instead of trying to pay it back threefold. Look over there. Who is that driving the white chariot?"

"It is Amphiaraus, a prophet as well as a brave soldier. He did not agree with Adrastus about this war, and had no wish to take part. Yet he was forced to come because he once swore that if they ever had a difference of opinion his wife, Eriphyle, would have the casting vote – and she obliged him to join the fight just for the sake of a jewel Polyneices offered her, although I must admit it was the fabled necklace of eternal youth which the goddess Aphrodite presented to her daughter Harmonia on her marriage to king Cadmus. Even so, the valiant Amphiaraus has taken up arms knowing that the Argives are doomed to be defeated, and that he himself will fall in battle."

"May his powers of vision prove true, as long as he and my brother are spared. But can you see Capaneus down there among them? I have heard he is a fearsome, savage warrior."

"He is the one who is pacing up and down beneath the

walls. You can be sure he is looking for a spot to scale them. He is an insolent and reckless man. He boasts that even if the gods wish otherwise he will enter Thebes and drag all its women off to slavery in Mycenae."

"O Zeus, send down your thunderbolts on this proud man who would have us carrying pitchers from the well to his high palace. I would prefer to die a thousand deaths than to endure such servitude!"

"A wise choice, my girl. But go inside for a while. You have seen the seven warlords and their forces. A company of women is coming this way, to make their plea for mercy to the gods."

"Very well. I shall leave you now – but come the moment you have news."

As Antigone withdrew into the palace, the women came and stood before the altar of Zeus. Raising their arms in supplication to the heavens, they began to chant:

> *Help us, o father Zeus, we pray!*
> *Save Thebes and us from Pelops' curse.*
> *Do not let brother brother slay –*
> *No evil in the world is worse.*
> *Let us not be dragged into slavery,*
> *With weeping and pain as company.*

... "o father Zeus, do not let brother brother slay"...

Let not the god who stalks our walls
With spiteful Eris at his side,
Fuelling hatred, firing passions,
Darkening our young men's minds,
Blind them to their love for life
And drag them into bloody war.
Drive stubborn Ares from our land
And, father Zeus, king of the gods,
Bring love between the brothers again.

But, alas, we know the concerns of men
Are far removed from those of the gods,
And Ares would not beat thus at our gates
If he intended to turn and go.
Nor will the angry Erinnyes,
Who struck down Iocaste, Oedipus, Laius,
Leave Eteocles and his brother unscathed.
We fear that their wrath will not be appeased
Till Thebes and its seven gates fall to the flames.
And yet, Zeus, you can, you can if you will
Lift from our city the dark threat of war.

Suddenly one of the women cried out, "Can I believe my eyes? Isn't that Polyneices who has just come into the city, and in full armour, too?"

"Yes, I am Polyneices. I had no difficulty slipping in over the wall. But may the gods help me if I have fallen into a trap and am seized. The Theban troops will leap on me like wild dogs. Let them just dare, and then they will see the stuff I'm made of, and how keenly this knife cuts. Besides, I am in a hurry to see Antigone."

"Have no fear," replied the tutor. "Here you are in no danger, and Antigone will be with us soon. Antigone! Antigone! Come quickly! The man you were so anxious to see is here. Ah, there she is! Quick girl, your brother's waiting. As for me, I'm going to take a walk along the ramparts, to find out what is happening."

"Dearest brother, come, let me embrace you! If only you hadn't left us. You should never have been sent away from here. We missed you terribly, you know. We heard that you got married, but in foreign parts, without our blessings, and with none of us there to celebrate with you. If only that were the worst of it! That foreign marriage of yours has brought disaster on us, Polyneices. If you two brothers had not quarrelled, all would be well now. But it is our fate to be hounded by the gods for crimes which our forebears committed – yet enough of that. This present war which hangs over our heads is what we must try to find a way of stopping."

"Antigone, dear sister, I have come here, braving every danger, because you asked to see me. The gods accepted the libations I poured out to them and helped me get across the walls without being spotted. But when I saw our house, the altars of the gods, the training grounds I practised on, and Dirce's fountain, tears sprang into my eyes and my heart hardened with resentment. For I was cast out from my country and forced to make my way in foreign lands. It cost me blood, toil, tears and sweat – and my brother is the one who did this to me."

"Do not say that, for you cannot know if Eteocles was to blame or if some god has decided to leave the house of Labdacus without an heir. Nor do I know what we can do to change things, if they have already been decided on Olympus. But we should at least try. That is why I sent word for you to come and have called for Eteocles as well. He should be here at any moment. Yet tell me, why is exile in a foreign land so terrible?"

"That, sister, you will only come to understand by living it."

"But if an exile lacks for nothing?"

"He still longs for his home and for his own folk, and worst of all, he lacks his freedom."

"Do you mean to say, he is not free to express his own opinions?"

"Yes, and must slavishly agree with every stupid word his powerful protectors say."

"Yet there is always hope."

"That is small consolation, and it becomes a mockery when that hope proves false."

"And how did you live before you married?"

"I often went to bed hungry, sister."

"But our parent's friends, did they not help you?"

"When such people see you fall, they all disappear!"

"At least our family name must have been some help to you."

"Titles don't fill one's stomach, Antigone."

"Yet you rose to high rank down in Argos."

"Yes, but that did not come about as you imagine."

"How did it happen, then?"

"Since you wish to hear, I'll tell you. It is a strange tale. Apollo had once made Adrastus a prophecy telling him he must marry his daughters to a lion and a wild boar, and of course, the poor man was completely at a loss. It was just about this time that I arrived in Argos, and being weary and half-starved, I went up to Adrastus' palace to ask for food and shelter. Right on my heels, another man arrived. He, too, had been banished from his country. His name was Tydeus, and he was the son of king Oeneus of Calydon. Like me, he was worn out and his clothes in tatters. They gave us a bite to eat, then led us off to the guest chamber to get some sleep. There was nothing in the room but a bed and a few rag mats spread upon the floor. Tydeus immediately told me that the bed was his, and haughtily pointed me towards the mats. I was insulted by his manner and let him have the sharp edge of my tongue. He cursed me for my insolence, and in a moment we were at each other's throats. Then we went for our swords and grabbed our shields to fight it out like soldiers. The duel was about to start when Adrastus himself appeared in the doorway. 'What is going on here?' he shouted angrily, but then his eyes fell on our shields. On mine the lion of Thebes was painted, while that of Tydeus carried a wild boar, the emblem of Calydon. 'Are you wild beasts, to fight like this?' Adrastus cried. 'Put up your swords and tell me who you are, and why you bear the lion and the boar upon your shields.' We explained our coats of arms to him, he told us of the prophecy, and the very next day he married his two daughters off to us. And that was not all. When we became Adrastus' sons-in-law, he promised he would set us up as kings upon our fathers' thrones. It was decided that the first of these two campaigns was to be launched against Thebes, since it lies much closer to Argos. Fortune smiled on me, you see. Luck and nothing more brought me the help I need to regain what I have so unfairly lost. As for the one who did me this injustice, let him think long and hard before he tries to pit himself against our might. There are seven of us, all resolute warlords – Adrastus, myself, Tydeus and four other chieftains from the Peloponnese – and we have a strong, determined army. I will not compromise on this. I have been through hard times in my banishment, and now I seek my father's throne. One can bear a noble name and still be a mere nobody. It's having the royal power that counts."

As he was saying this, the women suddenly cried out, "Eteocles is coming! May the gods reconcile the brothers!"

"Your moment has arrived, Antigone," said the eldest. "Perhaps you can help them with your sensible opinions."

"If they want help, that is. Come, Eteocles, here is your brother. You cannot imagine how happy the two of you have made me. Please do not spoil it all!"

"Well, here I am, sister, and I'm ready to do anything I can to please you. But this fellow here must show some sense of proportion first of all, and stop making such unreasonable demands."

"Brother," Antigone begged, "do not rush to judge and criticize. Consult your heart before you speak out or come to any decision. Forgive me for speaking to you in this way, but you have neither father to rebuke you nor a mother to turn to for advice. We sisters of yours are but weak creatures, and I know it is the old custom not to place any value on a girl's opinion. Try to imagine that it is your mother who speaks through my mouth, for if she lived, I know she would say the same things I am telling you. Take that angry look from your face, and stop all that furious huffing and puffing. Look your brother in the eye. It's not the Gorgon's head you have in front of you! And you, Polyneices, turn round at look at Eteocles. If you speak to his face, you'll choose your words more wisely, and he will listen to the things you have to tell him. Our mother used to say that if two friends fall out and want to make it up again, they must look each other in the eye and only remember what unites them. The rest they can forget for ever. Now, Polyneices, tell us why you have led this foreign army here. If you have been unjustly treated, then let some god be judge and hand down a wise verdict which will reconcile you with your brother."

"I'll speak out straight and simple, sister. When you are in the right, you don't need airy words and clever arguments. My case speaks for itself. Everyone knows that, as we had agreed, I handed power to my brother and he swore that once a year had passed he would relinquish it to me. Instead, he trampled on his oaths, clung to the throne, seized all my worldly goods and banished me as well. I, on the other hand, am willing once I get back what belongs to me to send the army home to Argos, reign for a year, then give him the kingdom for the next twelve months, just as we first agreed. I have no wish to pillage the city I was born in, nor would it give me any pleasure to scale its walls with ladders, but I shall do so if I do not get the justice which I seek. May the gods be my witness, I am doing this simply because I have been robbed of my birthright and my homeland. Could anything be plainer? Surely it is obvious to all that what I say is more than fair."

"Both fair and generous," remarked the leader of the listening women. "Now let Eteocles but speak with equal wisdom and we may all enjoy the peace your reconciliation brings."

"I shall certainly be reasonable," replied Eteocles, "though let me add that if all men meant the same thing by the word, they would never even quarrel, let alone make war. I admit that we can say in theory that such and such a thing is right or wrong, but there is a great difference between words and deeds. And when it comes to deeds, here's where I stand: I would strive to reach the stars, run countless leagues to meet the dawn or grasp the setting sun, descend into the bowels of the earth, were such things possible – but only to achieve one aim: to harness to my cause the greatest of all goddesses, Vasilia, symbol of earthly rule. Yet here is this fellow telling me to give it up when I already have it in my grasp! I ask you, were I to do what he demands, would you consider me a man of strength and judgment or merely a weak and foolish creature? Would it not be to my great and lasting shame if I were to step down from the throne simply because he has come here with an army and threatens to lay waste the land? It would

be another matter had he come in peace; then I would willingly have let him stay – but as for what he now demands, no,
I shall never do it. I will not give up the kingdom to become
his slave. Only a fool would do a thing like that. No! War, I
say! Let swords be drawn and the plain be filled with chariots! The throne is mine, and I will not let him have it! Even if
some injustice must at times be done to hold on to earthly
power, it can be justified as long as one is just and pious in all
other matters."

The listening women gasped in horror at what Eteocles
had said. "Why speak like this, my lord?" they asked in pro-
test. "Why do you praise inequity and trample justice in the
dust?"

"And, brother," added Antigone, "Why do you adore the
worst of goddesses, Philarchia, the love of power, above all
other deities? Why have you lost your head to her, when you
know all too well that wherever she worms her way into a
palace, she brings destruction in her wake? There are other
deities as well, you know. How come you have forgotten Isotis,
the spirit of equality, the only divinity who can bind brother
to brother and friend to loving friend? Without her aid we
should have neither true friendship nor peace. For when one
man has too much and the other all too little, nothing but
trouble can come of it. Consider how fairly those two sisters,
Day and Night, have divided up the hours between them. By

doing so, they have left no place for jealousy to breed, and live in harmony. Yet here you are, refusing to make a fair division of your power and fortune, blind to the fact that while Vasilia brings you strength and wealth, she does not protect you from suffering and disaster – for injustice and security do not go hand in hand. Do you think honours and glory are the be-all and the end-all of your life? Think well on it, and you will find they are not. Excess of wealth can only lead to ruin, and the reasonable man is happy with the bare necessities of life. Yet if I were to ask you whether you preferred the throne to the salvation of your country, I know which you would choose. Wait, though, till strong-walled Thebes falls to the Argive lances, its maidens dragged away in droves to slavery, and you will see your love of power turn to bitter ashes. You, too, Polyneices, behaved most foolishly when you fell in with Adrastus' proposal and launched this campaign against your native land. For if and when you ever enter the city as its conqueror, what kind of trophies will you have to show for it? How will you bring yourself to sacrifice to Zeus, or have the heart to adorn the temples with inscriptions such as, 'Polyneices, having razed Thebes to its foundations, dedicates these shields to the gods'? I hope you never have to taste so sour a victory. If, on the other hand, you meet defeat and manage to get back to Argos in one piece, leaving the fields of Thebes sown with the lifeless corpses of the Argive

army, how will you bear the shame of it when you overhear
folk saying, 'A fine pair of weddings you arranged, Adrastus.
We have paid for your daughters' marriages with the flower
of our youth'. No, Polyneices, you have not thought this
through wisely. Just like your brother, you have been stubborn and hot-headed! Put matters right, while there is still
time left, for there is nothing worse than madness joined to
madness."

"Antigone has spoken truly," cried the women with one
voice. "O, gods, drive off the evil cloud which hovers over
Thebes, and reconcile the sons of Oedipus."

"Enough of your advice!" snarled Eteocles. "We are merely
wasting time. There is only one way to reconcile us two, and
that is if I keep the reins of power in my hands. And you, who
long to take them from me, withdraw beyond the walls unless
you seek your death."

"Whoever kills me had better know that he will die by the
same stroke."

"Get out of here, I tell you – or perhaps you do not see
what I am holding in my hand?"

"I see, but I know how craven-hearted wealth is."

"So you brought your mighty army with you just to face a
coward?"

"A general must be sure of every step he takes, not rashly
bold."

"Yet I tell you that neither your overwhelming forces nor your libations to the gods will save your skin."

"Why not, since all I ask is what is mine by right?"

"We owe you nothing! Leave, I say!"

"Gods of my fathers! Look at the injustice of it. Hounding me from my own country!"

"You are the one who is hounding your country to destruction!"

"Ha, listen to the great oath-breaker!"

"Who are you to speak, traitor?"

"Usurper! You have stolen my throne from me!"

"I tell you one last time – there is nothing for you here in Thebes."

"Sister! You women, all of you – do you hear the man?"

"You are their enemy! Be gone!"

"Very well – but in the battle you will meet me face to face."

"I count the moments till I do."

"I shall be waiting at the seventh gate."

"And I'll be there to challenge you!"

"This is the end of us!" cried Antigone. "Are you determined to bring your father's curse on you?"

"What must be, must be! I won't give up the throne, even if this palace sinks beneath my feet."

"And I am cast out like a slave, as if Oedipus had never

been my father. But my sword will not lie idle – and if my country suffers for it, Eteocles is to blame, not I. I am going now. I bid farewell to all of you who feel for me, and cast a last fond look at the statues of the gods and this fair house, which I may never see again; although I live in hope of it, and believe that with the gods' help I shall defeat this fellow and his army and be crowned king upon my father's throne again. Now I must go where Fate commands."

"Go, and I shall be waiting for you. At the seventh gate your time of reckoning will come."

As the brothers turned on their heel and left, Antigone cried out, "No brothers, no! Not that! There are enough Thebans and Argives to decide the battle without your joining in!"

But Polyneices and Eteocles were deaf to her pleas. Antigone stood alone a moment in despair, then ran into the palace to sob her heart out unobserved, while the women stood murmuring gloomily among themselves.

"Alas, they will slaughter each other, the poor fellows," said one. "Instead of the throne of Thebes, they will earn themselves a seat in Hades."

"And all because they will neither of them see reason," another added.

"They are stubborn, filled with hatred and blinded by their lust for power."

"All we can hope is that some god will pity them and hold

... "At the seventh gate your time of reckoning will come"...

them back."

"None of them will. The gods all hate them. Besides, even they do not like to interfere with the Fates. Teiresias the seer said it plainly: 'They will fall on each other's swords and die'."

"A pity, a pity," sighed the women, breaking into a sad chant:

> *See the cruel trick the hard Fates have played,*
> *Inviting dread Ares to Bacchus's feast,*
> *The time when our youth drink the pleasures of life*
> *With dancing, gay song and wild revels till dawn.*
>
> *But the mad god of war has halted love's dance,*
> *Marched into the circle with drawn sword and spear,*
> *And with wild cries of rage and hot, smoking breath*
> *Has started his own dance of fire and death.*
>
> *Now Eris rejoices and crows with cruel glee*
> *That the brothers are parted by her vicious spite*
> *And the last of the Labdacids – unhappy breed!*
> *Will be wiped from existence, killed to a man*
> *As she piles misfortunes on suffering Thebes.*
>
> *O, lofty Cithaeron, home of the nymphs,*

Where Bacchus is honoured and Artemis roams,
If only you'd sunk into Tartarus
Instead of saving and rearing the child
Whom they brought to you, bound by the ankles, to die;
To ransom the young men and women of Thebes
And spare their poor mothers, who hate bloody war.

Yet you pitied the infant. How could you know
What the gods held in store for this man and his sons?
Those thrice-cursed sons who now sharpen their swords
To contest for the prize of Thebes' golden throne,
And threaten the land they were born in with fire.

Thebes, which was once beloved of the gods,
Founded by Cadmus, whose line traces back
To great Zeus himself. All the sons of the heavens
Came hastening here when weddings were held
And sat on the gold thrones Hephaestus had wrought
For the sake of Harmonia, whom he loved.
And Cadmus's daughter, the fair Semele,
Was chosen by Zeus to bring into the world
The god of the revels, the bringer of joy,
Dionysus-Bacchus, the Thebans' own god.
Again, by the will of the gods there was raised,
To the sweet-sounding echoes of Amphion's lyre,

This city of ours with its seven great gates
And its towering ramparts – beautiful Thebes.

Yet all for the sake of Ares' blood-lust
Thebes and its folk may be trampled to dust.

"Someone is coming," cried the leader of the women. "It is the tutor, and perhaps he has some news for us. Over here, teacher! You have been up on the ramparts, haven't you? What did you see?"

"I saw great things – but where is Antigone?"

"See where she comes."

"Old friend," Antigone asked anxiously, "do you know anything? Are my brothers still alive? Will the gates hold?"

"They are alive, my child. I could see it all from up there on the walls. The Argives have launched a strong attack, but our men are holding firm. I'll tell you everything from the beginning. Just before the fighting started, we heard their trumpets blare. Then a great war-cry went up and the trumpets sounded once again. With that, the enemy rushed to storm the gates and the battle was under way. At first they fought us from a distance, with bows and javelins, but when this failed to dent our line, Tydeus cried, 'Sons of Danaids, fall on those who hold the gates, before the defenders on the wall can mow us down with their arrows. Move cavalry and chariots to the

... "With that, the enemy rushed to storm the gates"...

attack!' Hearing his shouted orders, they threw themselves
upon us with drawn swords. A desperate struggle followed,
and the parched earth drank its fill of blood. Next, Parthenopaeus charged the gates. 'Bring fire and pickaxes!' he
roared, hoping to burn the gates and undermine the walls.
But as he scrabbled furiously, a huge boulder crashed down
on his blond head, and now his poor mother Atalanta will
never set eyes on her son again. The moment Eteocles was
sure that the gates were safe in that section of the wall, he ran
to see what was happening elsewhere and I followed as best I
could, anxious not to let him out of my sight. Soon I saw
Tydeus and a swarm of spearsmen raining their javelins on
the battlements. Our men had lost their nerve and run for cover,
but your brother forced them back up on the walls. Yet this
was nothing to the battle-lust which had taken hold of Tydeus.
You should have seen him! Balancing one ladder on another,
he was scrambling up the wall with his shield held high above
his head, shouting that not Zeus himself could stop him taking the city. It seems the great god must have heard him, for
he was just about to pull himself onto the ramparts when a
bolt of lightning struck him and sent his blackened body tum-
bling to the earth below. Seeing this, Adrastus realised that
Zeus was on the Thebans' side and pulled the Argive forces
back, while our men, drawing courage from this hopeful omen,
poured from the gates and fell upon the enemy. In a moment

they were locked in combat, sword clashing against spear in deadly thrust, filling the place with bodies piled on each other. That is as much as I have seen. So far, we have kept the walls intact, but whether our luck will hold out, only the gods can tell."

"You have told us a great deal, old friend," replied Antigone, "but there is one thing you have not said: have my two brothers found each other yet?"

"They are both living. What more can you want to know?"

"You are keeping something back from me. What is it?"

"I have brought good news – is that not enough?"

"No, it is not, if there is worse to come."

"Why spoil the happy tidings?"

"Now you begin to frighten me."

"I told you – your brothers are still living."

"With all respect, old friend, I insist you be more honest with me."

"Then since you press me, I must reveal what followed. After the incident I have told you of, Eteocles reached the seventh gate. Polyneices was on the other side with a large body of troops, crying out, 'The coward, the oath-breaker! See, he is afraid to come and face me!' Then, from the gate-tower, Eteocles shouted down, 'Here I am, Polyneices. Now you will see that whatever else Eteocles may be, he is no coward. Just wait till I get down!' He hurried from the ramparts, appeared in the gateway and ordered the trumpets to sound for silence. When the two armies had fallen quiet, he drew a deep breath and cried out in an echoing voice, 'Brave leaders of the Danaids, and all of you who have come to crush this city, and you Cadmeians, who have defended the land your fathers gave you with such valour, hear what my heart tells me to say to you! Do not throw your lives away for me or Polyneices. Lay down your arms along the whole front and let the two of us fight this battle out alone. If I should beat my brother, I will keep the throne – and if I am defeated, then he will take it and you Argives may go home. Enough of us have fallen on both sides.' Polyneices shouted his assent and his cry was taken up by all the Argives and the Cadmeians, who were delighted at the way this war was ending. Then the two brothers poured libations to the gods and appointed Zeus as judge to ensure they would fight fairly. When the oaths were sworn, they buckled on their swords and each picked up his lance. Finally, they measured out the distance and stood facing each other with angry glares, eager to hurl their deadly weapons. That is where I left, for though I have fought in many battles and seen dreadful things, my old heart could not bear the sight of two brothers fighting a duel to the death."

"Yet I beg you, friend, lead me there. Perhaps I still have time to stop..."

"The end has come!" gasped a herald who now staggered

in.

"What end?" cried Antigone in alarm.

"The brothers are both dead. They died upon each other's swords!"

"Alas!" sobbed Antigone and fell wailing into the women's arms.

"Hear that, O royal palaces!" cried one of them. "The sons of Oedipus are no more. Their lust for power and their bitter spite have finished them."

"It was the disrespect they showed towards their father," said another.

"No, their black fate has killed them!" cried a third. "Apollo willed that they should pay for Laius's old sins."

"O, gods!" cried Antigone, "Since you are bent on hounding down this royal house, I am ready to pay now, in my turn, if it has come."

"The gods are not unjust, my child," rejoined the teacher. "What have you done, or your sister, for that matter, to be punished?"

"If we are not to blame ourselves, our blood is. Just as they punish the unjust, the gods are harsh towards the innocent who bear the sins of others. Such are the holly laws, and it is not our place to doubt them. Yet why should all of Thebes be made to pay? Will the Argives really leave off now, or will they fall upon the city and burn it to the ground?"

"Fear not, my child," the tutor reassured her, "The gods have decided that the city should be saved. Teiresias said so, and his prophecies have never proved false. Their own seer, Amphiaraus, was of the same opinion. Besides, Thebes is strongly defended. All our commanders have taken up position."

"I hope so. But you, herald, did you hear by any chance whether my brothers said anything before they died? Did they give any orders or make any last request of us who are left behind?"

"Nothing of that sort reached my ears. I heard only what they said before the combat started. Each of them begged the gods – the insolence of it! – to help him kill his brother. First Polyneices, turning toward Argos, called upon Hera to protect him. 'O Hera, reverend goddess,' he called out, 'you who guard Argos, I, too, am your subject; for my wife is the daughter of your city's king, and it was with an Argive army that I came to Thebes. For both these reasons, help me to kill this man who faces me and ascend my father's throne victorious.' Those were his very words, and I can tell you, they caused quite a stir of disapproval. Then Eteocles turned to face the temple of Athena and prayed aloud, 'Daughter of Zeus, grant me the victory. May I kill this man who has come to lay waste to his own city.' The way he said it, you would have thought his opponent was some stranger, and not the king's own brother. Finally, the trumpet sounded for the mortal combat to begin. For some time neither of them gained the upper hand, till Polyneices caught Eteocles a glancing blow upon the leg. The Argives whooped with joy – but not for long. A moment later, Eteocles tricked his brother into lifting up his shield. Quick as a flash he plunged his sword into the unprotected body, and Polyneices fell to the ground mortally wounded. Eteocles let out a shout of triumph and stooped to take the shield as a trophy. But there was life in Polyneices yet, and he somehow found the strength to deliver a death-blow of his own. The king fell at his brother's side and off they went to Hades, both of them. That's all I know. If they said anything before they died, I was too far away to catch their words, and besides, I came as fast as I could to bring the awful news."

"Ah, brothers!" cried Antigone. "You wouldn't listen to the voice of reason and now the flower of our royal line lies dead."

"Ill-fated men, your greed has brought you low," declared the leader of the women. "You lusted for kingly power and glory, but all you have gained is the dark halls of Hades."

"Alas! Disaster has rained down on us like hammer-blows. We have wept over our father's cruel misfortunes, mourned our poor mother, shed tears at banishments and hatred between brothers. Now we have no tears left, but only a heavy, dull ache in our hearts."

Looking at Antigone with pity in their eyes, the women broke into this grief-stricken cry:

> *O angry ones, Erinnyes,*
> *Your vile work is now achieved.*
> *Or do you have worse evil still*
> *To wound us with, a final blow?*
>
> *First you struck Laius down: and though*
> *Many are caught in Eris' web,*
> *What a foul death you saved for him –*
> *To die at the hand of his own child!*
>
> *Next you reserved for Oedipus*
> *The worst fate that a man could know.*
> *He who had saved the land of Thebes*
> *And toppled the dread Sphinx from her throne*
> *Was toppled himself, most horribly,*
> *And into Hades stumbled, blind.*
>
> *Now his two sons have been sent on that road*
> *By this, your last, and most terrible blow.*
> *Brother kills brother and is killed*
> *Their murderous hatred for ever quenched.*

... "Two slayers, two victims; two yards of land
Are now all they claim in the town of their birth"...

Two slayers, two victims; two yards of land
Are now all they claim in the town of their birth.

Enough, frightful Erinnyes! Leave us in peace
To swallow our bitterness and make moan.
This city has had enough of woes
And its suffering palace can take no more blows.

The women broke off as they saw a figure approaching. "Why, it is Creon!" one of them exclaimed. "He is going to make some announcement, listen."

Mounting the steps which led up to the battlements, Creon looked down and cried, "Honoured daughter of king Oedipus, mothers, wives and sisters of our brave Theban warriors, and all of you who hear me, I bring you joyful tidings. The city is saved! The Argive army did not wish to leave in peace, but they paid dearly for trying to seize our city. In the battle which followed, the gods accorded us a mighty victory. When it had ended, of all the seven Argive warlords only Adrastus saved his skin, and he fled with what little of his forces still remained. Now is not the time to tell you how all this came about, for I have something else to announce. Since the king has been killed, the only rightful heir to his throne is I, Eteocles' uncle and his closest relative. I received the command from his own lips before he died. He begged me to take his place and manage the affairs of Thebes, to care for his two sisters and in particular to celebrate the marriage between Antigone and my dear son Haemon with all due ceremony. He had one other order for me, too – his last and deepest wish: we are to leave the body of Polyneices unburied where it lies, outside the walls, to be devoured by the wild dogs and the vultures, and condemn his spirit to eternal wandering. May his fate be a warning to any who would seek to harm our land! If any man here dares to bury him, he will pay for that disobedience with his death. Such was Eteocles' last command. and I, by his will and the gods', am now the ruler of this city. It is my duty to obey your dead king's wishes, a duty I most willingly perform, for the law binds me and all of you to this, and justly so, moreover."

"Whether the law is just or not, only the gods can know," replied the women. "One thing is sure, however: it is so harsh that nobody will dare to disobey it."

They recoiled in horror when Antigone cried, "I shall!"

"What did you say?" gasped Creon. "I never dreamed that you could speak so foolishly."

"If there is any foolishness, it lies in what you seek to do."

"Eteocles gave the decree, and I am duty-bound to follow it."

"Yet what if that decree is wicked? Does it make no difference to you?"

"So you consider it unjust to leave Polyneices' body to the beasts?"

"Both unjust and in defiance of the law – for the gods' unwritten laws are higher than the laws of men."

"Yet has not Polyneices done his motherland great harm?"

"Whatever punishment was due to him the gods have meted out."

"And shall men not be allowed to punish even those who are traitors to their cities?"

"Let them be punished while they are still alive, but never after death."

"But he was steeped in guilt."

"He only asked for what was due to him."

"Enough of this! He will remain unburied."

"I beg you, in my mother's, your dead sister's name. Withdraw this cruel decree!"

"Begging will get you nowhere."

"Then let me wash his body, at least."

"I have told you: you will do this man no honours."

"Let me just kiss my brother one last time."

"Go on like this, and there will be no wedding with my son."

"And if I disobey you?"

"I say he was a traitor, and you will not pay him any last respects."

"I cannot call him traitor when his fate was written by the gods."

"Yet that is what he was and that is why he shall lie unburied and unmourned."

"Never! I shall find some way of burying him."

"Do that and you will find yourself in the same grave."

"What greater happiness than to share it with the brother whom I loved?"

"This is my last word, Antigone. Take care, for you are marching to your doom!"

"Creon, you cannot touch me with your threats. I shall do my duty. Do yours as you see fit. As to who owed the truer debt, let future generations be the judge."

"O Erinnyes, O angry ones," The women cried,

> *"O Erinnyes!"*
> *Now you have struck a worse blow still*
> *The mortal stroke we feared would fall.*
> *Now you have doomed them, one and all*
> *And the house of Oedipus is brought low.*
> *We hesitate which way to go;*
> *The path of prudence cries 'Obey!';*
> *Duty says 'No!'. Whichever way,*
> *We envy you, brave, unhappy maid*
> *As you march to your sacrifice, unafraid.*

ANTIGONE
After Sophocles

In the palace yard at Thebes, as rosy-fingered Dawn spread her golden mantle over the suffering city, Antigone was pacing nervously, when the doors opened and her younger sister appeared.

"Ismene," she burst out, "do you know of any misfortune that has not struck us yet, from all the many that Apollo prophesied? Bitterness, pain, shame and contempt – all these we have endured and worse. Doom and black death have fallen on our family. And now, as if these were not enough, comes Creon's dreadful order. Or perhaps you have not heard of this new evil that comes knocking at our gates, one only a deadly enemy could devise?"

"Your words astound me, Antigone, for I have heard nothing, whether good or evil. From the moment when our brothers were both killed and the Argive army left, defeated, no news has reached my ears that could make me either more or less miserable than before."

"I thought it must be so. That is why I wished to meet you here outside the palace, where we can be alone."

"Why, what has happened? Something terrible, I fear."

"It is, Ismene. The noble Creon has decreed that only one of our dead brothers is worthy of a grave, and that the other must lie where he fell, unburied. And so Eteocles, who by Creon's reckoning has done his duty to his country, will be interred with all the pomp that will give him an honoured place among the dead, while Polyneices, who is stretched out lifeless in a pool of blood, will go unmourned and unburied, food for the wild dogs and the birds of prey. This is what our 'pious' Creon has decided, and it is said he gave the order with us two in mind – me in particular, for he knows me well. Any moment now he will come in person to announce his order and warn us that whoever dares defy him will be put to shameful death by stoning. Now you know all, and the time has come for you to show whether you are a worthy daughter of a man who did not fail when duty called."

"If that is how things are, what can I do, unhappy sister?"

"You must decide if you will help me in this holy task."

"What do you wish to say? Speak clearly."

"I am asking you to help me carry off the body."

"Do you mean you are planning to bury the very man whose burial you have just told me is forbidden?"

"That man was my brother and yours, too. I shall not betray him."

"Are you mad, sister? How can you dream of disobeying such an order?"

"No one has the right to forbid me to carry out my duty."

"Antigone, dear, be reasonable. Remember how our father was humiliated when he laid bare his deeds for all to see, without considering what would come of it. In the end, they were more than he could bear to see himself, and he gouged his eyes out. Then think of our mother, who put a dreadful end to her own life because of the shame she had brought upon herself. A third blow fell when our two brothers threw themselves upon each other like mad dogs and died the worst of deaths. And consider what our fate will be if we two, all alone now as we are, set ourselves against the law by challenging the authority of the king. Do not forget, dear sister, that we are women. We cannot hope to defy those who hold power. Our lot is to bow our heads and be obedient in worse cases still. That is why I shall submit in this. All I can do is beg my brother in my heart to show me understanding, for I cannot try to be what I am not."

"Enough! I see I was wrong to seek your help. I no longer want it. I shall bury my brother all alone. What if I die for it? I shall defy the law, but I shall be faithful to my duty. And when I find myself in Hades I shall be happier in the company of those whose hearts were gladdened by my actions than I should be with those who are left here. As for you, betray the ones you love if that is what you prefer."

"I am not betraying them. I simply lack the strength to pit myself against the state."

"Then look for excuses to console yourself. I shall go to honour my dead brother."

"I tremble to think of the terrible price that you may pay for it."

"Save your own skin, and don't trouble your conscience over me."

"Why be so impetuous? At least take care that no one discovers your intentions."

"Tell them yourself. Shout the news out. I don't need your protection."

"You have a warm heart, sister, but it is a cold task you have set yourself."

"What matter, if cold limbs are warmed by what I do?"

"But you will never succeed."

"I shall go to bury him. I do not know if I shall succeed. Nothing is certain – but go I will."

"It is always wise to weigh one's chances before taking action."

"Be silent, lest you make me hate you! And do not approach the dead man, either, lest he hate you too – for ever. Leave me to my madness. The worst that I can suffer is death for carrying out my duty."

"Then go your way, rash sister. At least, where you are going, you will be among the ones you love, and loved in turn."

With these words, Ismene went back into the palace and Antigone turned from the gates. As she left, a group of Theban elders came and formed a circle. Raising their arms towards the heavens, they cried out:

O sun, with your golden beams
You have banished the shadows of night,
And with them you have cast out
The savage invader who came
With chariots by the score,
Bright shields and tufted helms.

Polyneices led him here;
He was brought by injustice and hate.
Like the eagle, with cruel, harsh cry
He came to dismember Thebes.

He circled the city with murderous spears;
He threatened our towers with ruin and fire,
Our wives and our children with slavery.
But he left in confusion, bloody and shamed,
When our dragon-born warriors shattered his ranks.

For the lord of Olympus hates impious words.
He loathes the braggart, despises conceit;
And he hurled his thunderbolt at the man
Who was ready to trumpet his victory
From the ramparts of seven-gated Thebes.
Burnt to a cinder he tumbled headlong,
He who had boasted he'd burn the town,
And what if the gods willed otherwise?
This signalled the end of the insolent Seven,
Who had dreamed of offering trophies to Zeus
When, all the while, he hated them.

Yet the brothers, those two unfortunate ones
Who shared the same father, the same child-bed,

... "What death can be blacker, more horrible
Than when brother kills brother in his turn?"...

Earned the most bitter of deaths for themselves.
What death can be blacker, more horrible
Than when brother kills brother in his turn?

But now that victory has crowned Thebes,
Let us forget the horrors of war
And run to the temples, all of us,
To honour Dionysus in dance
And sing hymns of praise to our saviour, Zeus.

"But look, the king is coming," cried the leader of the elders. "Now we shall learn why he has called us here and what he has to say."

"Men of Thebes!" cried Creon, when he drew near, "Having threatened our city with destruction, the gods have raised Thebes up again. I have sent for you because I know the great respect you have always shown for kingly power: first towards Laius, then to Oedipus, and finally his two sons. Now they are dead in mortal combat, brother against brother, I, as you know, have assumed the royal mantle as their closest relative. As king, I will expect you to judge me by my works. For I believe that he who rules a city is unworthy of the power he wields if he does not put the well-being of its citizens above all else, but out of fear does things which harm his people. Likewise, whoever puts a friend above his country is of no account. For I – and let Zeus be my witness if I do not speak the truth – would never hold my tongue if I saw disaster threaten, and I would never give the hand of friendship to any enemy of ours. Our land must be like a stout ship which does not fear the storm, and only among its loyal crew, our people, can trusted friends be found. It is on such a course that I shall steer this city, and make her stronger still by doing so. In accordance with these principles, I have come to a decision regarding the two sons of Oedipus. I have ordered that Eteocles be buried with all the honours owed to a brave king who dies defending his own country. But as for Polyneices, he returned from exile to lay waste the land where he was born, to spill his brother's blood, burn down our houses and lead the Thebans off in chains as slaves. Thus, I have given my command that no one weep for him, nobody offer the rites due to the dead, but that he lie unburied to be eaten by the vultures. I have decided this because I will never have it said of me that I place the unjust higher than the just. No, I will do honours only to the good and pious, whether they be alive or dead."

"Son of Menoeceus," replied the leader of the elders, "You are our king now and so it is you who will decide both for the dead and those of us still living. You have the right to make whatever laws you wish."

"Then see to it that no one disobeys my orders."

"Can you not place that burden on younger shoulders than ours?"

"I have already done so. I have put guards to watch over the dead body."

"Then what do you wish of us?"

"If anyone dares to defy my wishes, I demand that you refuse him all support."

"But nobody would dream of doing such a thing – unless he wanted to bring destruction on himself."

"Yes, death will be the price, be sure of that. Yet there are many here mistaken enough to think that they might gain by it."

"Your majesty!" cried out a guard who now came running in, "your majesty, if you see me in this state, it's not because I'm out of breath. Time and again I stopped on my way, half minded to retrace my steps for fear that you might punish me. But then again, I asked myself, if Creon learns of this from other lips, won't I still be punished? So, with a heavy heart I set off once again, and the short distance seemed to drag on endlessly, so hesitant were my steps. In the end, I decided to come here and tell you. After all, I thought, I can suffer nothing worse than what the Fates have already decided for me."

"So what is troubling you? Speak man!"

"Yes, but first I want to tell you that I didn't do anything. Why, I didn't even see whoever carried out the wicked deed.

It wouldn't be fair if I was made to pay for it – I'm innocent!"

"Trying to make things easy for yourself, eh? That means you must have something terrible to reveal."

"Yes, terrible. That's why I'm so afraid."

"So, hurry up and tell us what it is. Then get out of my sight, if that is what you want."

"Well then, I'll tell you. Not many hours past, honours were done to Polyneices' corpse! Whoever it was threw earth over it, made the traditional offerings to the dead, then disappeared before we could catch sight of them."

"What did you say, fellow! Who dared to do this thing?"

"That I cannot tell you. All I know is that no pick was used to do the digging, and whoever did it left no clues. When the morning watch showed us what had happened, we did not know what to think. The dead man had disappeared, not into a tomb of course, just covered with a sprinkling of fine earth. We guards began to quarrel then, throwing the blame on one another, but each man claimed that he knew nothing. We were willing to lay our hands on red-hot iron, to throw ourselves into a flaming furnace and to swear by all the gods that we had neither done the thing ourselves, nor seen whoever did it, nor even knew of anyone that might dream of doing such a thing. To cut a long story short, someone finally said we must run and tell you what had happened. None of us could deny that, but nobody was willing to come. So we drew lots and I,

poor fellow, pulled the shortest straw. So, here I am – and no
happier at being here than you are to see me, for I know a
bearer of bad news is never welcome."

"Your majesty," said the leader of the elders, "something
tells me that whatever may have happened, it was done at the
bidding of some god."

"Be silent, lest you draw my anger down upon you! Why,
a mere child would not say such a thing, let alone an elder
whose long experience should have taught him wisdom. How
in the world could the gods take pity on a man who returned
to his own country to burn its temples, and lay waste his ancestral lands, trampling divine law in the dust? Or do you
believe the gods do honour to criminals? No, I'll tell you how
it happened: there are certain people in this city who are mut-
tering behind closed doors, who do not respect my power or
the rule of law. They must have paid to have this done. Nothing corrupts like money. It topples castles and drives people
from their homes; it buys men's minds and leads them into
evil ways. Whoever was paid to do this wicked deed, he will
not escape my wrath. Hear me, and hear me well: as much as
I respect and honour Zeus, if you do not find the man who
buried Polyneices, you will die a slow and painful death for
it. I shall force from you every word you know concerning
this forbidden act, to teach everyone a lesson that profit must
be earned by honest labour, not by treachery – for money ill-

gained does more to ruin a man than make his fortune."

"Will you let me say a word before I go?" the guard enquired.

"Why? To wound me deeper still?"

"But I shall wound you in the ears, not in the soul."

"And what might that mean, pray?"

"Something very true, my lord. The one who wounded you to the soul was the one who carried out the deed."

"Fellow, you're nothing but a windbag."

"Yes, if your majesty so pleases, but I am not the one who did this act."

"What if I say you are?"

"My lord, you must use judgement when you judge."

"So now we play with words, eh? Enough of this! I shall go inside, and if when I return you do not point out the culprits to me, you will learn that money earned by bribery does not come as cheaply as you think."

With this, Creon turned on his heel and strode back into the palace.

"Well, I hope we lay our hands on them," remarked the guard. "We'll be lucky if we do, though. In any case, don't expect to see my face round here again. I got off lightly, may the gods be thanked, and I'm leaving while the going's good."

Bidding the elders farewell, the guard took a hasty leave. Once more, they took up their chant, this time in a thoughtful, puzzled voice.

> *This world holds many wonders*
> *But none is greater than man.*
> *He has tamed the foaming seas,*
> *Driving roads across the waves.*
> *Earth, the greatest goddess,*
> *Is subjected to his plough*
> *And yields abundant tribute.*
> *By the power of his mind*
> *He rules the animal world.*
> *Horn and hoof and feather*
> *Both live and die for him.*
>
> *He has mastered speech and writing*
> *And with his brilliant gifts*
> *Has built himself fair cities,*
> *Temples and monuments.*
> *With a chisel in his hand*
> *He gives dead marble life*
> *And with a simple paintbrush*
> *He can make a blank wall breathe.*
> *The Muses and the Graces*
> *Come running at the call*
> *Of whoever serves and worships*

Music, dance and song
Or divinely-inspired poetry.
With his fine and lovely arts
Man, creator and instructor,
Lifts his life high aloft
And raises it to the skies.

But only if he so wishes.
For while man can achieve
So many wonderful things,
He cannot escape from evil;
And from good things to bad
His mind soon runs with ease.
And then we grieve to see
Man shrink from giant to dwarf.

"But what do I see?" cried the leader of the elders. "The guard is coming back again, and he is dragging Antigone! O miserable daughter of the unhappy Oedipus, can you have flouted the king's law and been caught in some rash act?"

"Here's your culprit, masters! We caught her burying the body. Now, where's Creon?"

"Here he comes – as if he'd guessed!"

"Guessed what? What is this I see?"

"Your majesty, I hadn't intended to return, I was so fright-

ened by your threats. But even if I'd sworn an oath on it, I'd
have gone back on my word to bring this lawbreaker to you.
For when you know that you have just escaped some terrible
danger, there's nothing to compare with the sweet relief it
brings. There was no need to cast lots this time, I can tell you.
It was I who grabbed her by the arm and brought her here.
She's yours now. Interrogate the girl, then deal with her as
you see fit. As for me, I'm sure that you'll agree that after
this, the last thing I deserve is punishment."

"But why did you arrest her? Speak!"

"She is the one who has been trying to bury the body. Now
you know it all."

"I do not understand what you are saying."

"Your majesty, I tell you I caught her sprinkling earth on
the very man whose burial you have forbidden. Don't I make
myself clear?"

"Where did you see her, fellow? How did you catch her?"

"It happened like this. I went back to my post, my ears still
ringing with your threats. The other guards and I scraped the
earth from off the body, and when we had got it all cleaned up
we sat down on the rocks to keep a watch, nudging each other
from time to time in case our eyelids drooped and the body
was covered up again without our noticing. The sun was high
in the sky and it was starting to get hot when a violent whirlwind struck, like the anger of some god. All over the plain,

...“a violent whirlwind struck, like the anger of some god”...

branches were torn from trees and the sky was filled with such a flurry of fallen leaves and dust that we had to close our eyes against it. As soon as the divine rage had subsided, this girl appeared, and the moment she saw the corpse uncovered she let out a heart-rending cry and threw herself upon it. Like a goldfinch that returns to find an empty nest and her young ones gone, she uttered sad cries of distress and began to curse whoever had dug her brother up. Then she took earth in her hands and threw it on the body, sprinkling the grave with wine poured from a bronze vessel. Before she could finish the rite, we rushed over and arrested her. We questioned her both about what we had just seen and the previous episode. She admitted everything so calmly that if I were not so glad I'd saved my own skin, I would have pitied her; for it's not pleasant to see someone that we are fond of in such a terrible plight. Sorry as I was, I brought her here – after all, I had to save my own neck, and that's what matters most."

"Hey, you!" barked Creon, "You with your head so meekly bowed, do you confess to all this, or are you going to deny it?"

"I deny nothing. It all happened exactly as he said."

"Guard, I have no further need of you. You are free and acquitted of all charges. Now, Antigone, tell me: how could you dare to do this thing? Don't say you didn't know it was forbidden, and what the punishment would be."

"I knew. I did it because the prohibition did not come from Zeus, and neither has Divine Justice laid down any such law for men. I cannot conceive how the commands of a mere mortal could presume to trample on the unwritten laws of the gods, laws which have always been and always will be. I could not bear to transgress against this eternal edict and chose to face the punishment of men, rather than have Divine Justice fall upon me. If I am to die before my time, I shall count it a blessing, for in this life I have known nothing but pain and misfortune. If I had left my brother unburied, I would have dragged out a life of double misery. What does it trouble me if my act seems foolish to a man who is himself so foolish as to go against the wishes of the gods?"

"This girl is hard as stone," one of the elders said. "Just like her father. He wouldn't budge an inch, although he saw disaster coming."

"You will soon learn that nothing but humiliation comes to those who are too proud to see when they must yield," said Creon. "Hard things are easily shattered. Consider iron, both the cast and forged. One breaks because it is brittle, the other survives because it knows how to bend. The savage horse is easily broken in with a small, pliant bridle. The small man cannot stand up against the mighty one who has the backing of the law, yet here she stands, having transgressed that law herself, flaunting her deed in insolent pride before me, as if she were my equal. Or perhaps she thinks she rules this land, not I! Perhaps she would, at that, if I let her go unpunished. That is why she must be dealt with without mercy, even if she is my sister's child and thus my closest relative. She and Ismene are in this thing together. Bring her here, too – I saw her tear her hair when she heard her brother would be left to lie unburied. Those who secretly plot lawless deeds sometimes betray themselves too easily!"

"Do you plan more wickedness, then? Is my death not enough for you?"

"Do not trouble yourself. When that is done, I need take no further steps."

"Then why delay? Neither of us finds any pleasure in this conversation, so have done with it and give me the end I long for. How else could I earn such praise and honour, but in doing my duty in burying my dead brother – a duty forbidden to me by a powerful but foolish ruler? You should know that everybody here would say the same, were their tongues not paralysed with fear. That is a tyrant's weakness – he says and does whatever he thinks fit, without so much as listening to what his people think."

"How dare you speak like this, when there is not a voice in Thebes to back you up?"

"They all agree with me, although their lips are sealed. They do not speak out for fear of angering you."

"Do you find it fitting to behave so differently from these wise elders?"

"It is my brother I am honouring, not theirs."

"And was Eteocles a stranger to you? How come that you do honours to the one and spurn the other?"

"Not even that other whom you speak of would say such a thing."

"Yet it was Polyneices whom they caught you weeping over."

"He was my brother, not some stray dog!"

"But a traitor, while Eteocles was a patriot."

"In Hades, the same honours are accorded all the dead."

"You cannot put good and evil on the same footing."

"In the underworld, no such distinctions are made."

"An enemy does not become a friend, even when he is dead."

"I am their sister, and I was born to love them, not to hate them."

"Then love them from your grave. For as long as I am in this world, no woman shall rule here."

"Here comes Ismene," one of the elders cried. "Tears are running down her cheeks and her lovely face is clouded by the dark hollows of her eyes."

"Come here, you! Viper that you are, you planned to drink my blood. Little did I guess that I was harbouring a double threat within my own four walls, a pair who were plotting my destruction. Come now, will you confess you were a party to this burial or are you going to swear sweet innocence?"

"Yes, I helped. We share responsibility."

"Sister, you did not help at all. You neither wanted to, nor would I let you."

"When I see you facing such misfortunes all alone, I will deny nothing and not fear to stand beside you."

"All those in Hades know I carried out the task unaided. I have no need of your words of support."

"They are not just words. I wish to die and honour our dead brother with you."

"I neither want to see you dead nor take upon yourself deeds which you had no hand in. My own death will suffice."

"And what joy will I have left in life when you are gone?"

"Ask Creon. Do you not care for him?"

"Sister, what can you hope to gain by embittering me in this way?"

"You think my words do not leave a bitter taste in my own mouth?"

"And yet I long to help you."

"You will make me happy by escaping."

"Let me share your fate!"

"No, you have chosen life – I, death."

"Are you sure you know the reason why?"

... "will you confess you were a party to this burial
or are you going to swear sweet innocence?"...

"It is a reason which appeals to some. Those in the under-world would appreciate my motives."

"Yet we both bear equal responsibility. We each love our dead brother just as much."

"You are alive still, Ismene. I am as good as dead already. Be brave, little sister."

"They are both mad!" cried Creon. "One of them shows it now, the other was crazy from the moment she was born."

"When one faces misery, one throws caution to the winds," replied Ismene. "I cannot bear the thought of living if my sister dies."

"Forget about her. She no longer exists."

"What! Will you kill your own son's fiancee?"

"There's no shortage of women in this world."

"Would you separate such a loving couple – and by death?"

"I do not wish my son to have a wife who is a rebel."

"Ah, Haemon, your own father is wounding you to the soul!"

"Enough! Say no more of this marriage!"

"Would you truly put an end to such a union?" enquired the leader of the elders.

"Enough, I said! This wedding will be cancelled by her death!"

"Alas! It is decided, then."

"By me, by you, and the entire city. Take her inside, slaves,

and guard her well. Even the bravest hearts strive to escape
their fate."

   With a groan, the elders began to speak once more.

> *Lucky are those who in this life*
> *Have never tasted bitterness.*
> *For when a god's wrath strikes at them*
> *Their troubles will come thick and fast,*
> *Tumbling them like the foaming waves*
> *The wild north wind swells in rage*
> *As the shores they beat on moan in pain.*

> *Three generations without cease*
> *Disaster has struck at the Labdacids*
> *And each generation in its turn*
> *Has been snared in the nets of cruel Fate.*
> *Now, when at last some faint hope gleamed,*
> *The Erinnyes have turned men's minds*
> *And Hades sharpens his cruel sword.*

> *No mortal can tame your power, O Zeus.*
> *Almighty Sleep could never o'ercome it,*
> *Nor Time, that great changer, make its mark.*
> *Ageless you rule the world, O Zeus,*
> *From High Olympus' golden halls;*

And your will shall always remain the same:
That no mortal man may go far in this world
Without meeting misfortune, bitterness, pain.

Hope brings relief to many men,
But as many again does hope delude,
Sending all they have striven for up in flames.
Wise indeed was the man who said
That evil seems good to those whose minds
The god has clouded.

But Haemon comes, The last and dearest of the king's
*   sons,*
Anguish is written on his face –
For he now knows all that has taken place.

"Father," said Haemon as soon as he drew near, "I was raised to manhood on your wise counsel, and I shall heed it now. Your opinion is what comes first with me. My marriage must come second."

"Well spoken, Haemon. Children must never place anything higher than their father's word. When he is strengthened by their loyal support, his enemies tremble and true friends are rewarded. Woe to the man whose children prove worthless. All he brings into the world is a host of troubles, and he becomes the dupe of all around him. Mark what I say, and do not let some maiden turn your mind. The embrace of an evil woman will not warm your heart, but chill it. There is nothing worse than to have a wicked companion in your house. So let that girl of yours go off and marry Hades. She is the only person in this whole city who has flouted my command, and I do not intend to make a fool of myself by going back on my word. I gave fair warning, and my decision stands. If we start showing mercy to our own family, we shall soon find ourselves having to tolerate the disobedience of strangers; but when I am just in my own home, then my citizens, too, will trust me to do justice, and know that if any of them defies the laws and goes against my will, they will get no prizes for it. When the city chooses a ruler, all must abide by his decisions – big or small, just or otherwise, it matters not. For the ruler will even throw himself into the flames if the common good dictates it, and to his faithful subjects he will be faithful to the end. Discipline alone can save a city. When lawlessness creeps in, the city rocks on its foundations, houses tumble and whole armies are put to flight. That is why we must be stern guardians of the law and not fly in its face, especially at some female whim. If it were a man I faced, things might be different, but I will not have it said that I retreated because of a mere girl."

"Father, the gods have given man his mind, the most precious possession he will ever have upon this earth. I could never dream you might be wrong in this, but there are those who may think otherwise. As your son, it is my duty to pay heed to how men judge your actions, in case they find grounds for accusing you. The people of Thebes tremble at the sight of you, and would never say things in your presence which might give offence. But I know what is said behind your back, and I am obliged to tell you. The truth is, father, the city is weeping for the maiden. Men mutter that she is being sent unjustly to an ignoble death for having carried out a noble deed. They claim she did a splendid thing to bury her dead brother instead of leaving him to be devoured by scavenging beasts. It is the highest praise that she deserves, they say, not execution. Father, there is nothing nearer to my heart than to see you reign in happiness, loved by your subjects. What joy could be greater than the good name and good fortune of my father? But you are losing that good name, and I, who know it, am in duty bound to warn you. Do not be guided by your own opinions solely, for whoever believes that he alone is right and no other man his match in bravery or judgement will one day be revealed a hollow man. A wise ruler is not ashamed to learn from others, and nobody should be unyielding. All of us know which trees survive on the banks of roaring torrents – only those which bend their branches to the wind and water, while those which stand rigid and unbending

... "The truth is, father, the city is weeping for the maiden"...

are torn up by the roots. It's the same with ships: when the
captain keeps the rigging taut in a gale, the vessel's lost. I
know I am younger than you, but I, too, can be right. And
that, father, is why I advise you to put aside your wrath and
change your mind. No man born knows everything. All of us
make mistakes, and a man must always profit by whatever
words of wisdom reach his ears, whoever may have spoken
them."

"Your majesty," added the leader of the elders, "if your
son has spoken reasonably, then give his words some thought.
And you, young man, do likewise, for there is much truth in
what both of you have said."

"So we greybeards must take lessons from a stripling, eh?"

"Only reject what is not true, father, and don't pay any
attention to my youth if what I say is right."

"So, is it right to honour evil men?"

"I could never imagine doing such a thing."

"But is this girl not stained with evil?"

"That is not what they are saying in the city."

"So now the city will tell me what to do, is that it?"

"Now it is you who are talking like a child, for the city is
not yours alone but everybody's."

"Then what is left to me?"

"Only a man who rules over an empty desert can take a
decision without asking for a second opinion."

"So, young man, you have chosen a woman for your ally, eh?"

"It is you who are my ally – and I do not think you are a woman."

"How dare you mock me, insolent wretch!"

"If I do so, it is because my heart is torn by your injustice."

"I am unjust when I do honour to my kingly rank?"

"You do that rank no service when you flout the divine laws."

"Miserable cur, you have become her slave!"

"I will not bow before your evil plans."

"I suppose you're saying all this for her sake?"

"And for yours, and mine, and for the gods of Hades."

"Then mark my words, young cub, and mark them well: I will never give you back the girl alive."

"If she dies, then another will die with her."

"Do you dare to threaten me?"

"I would not dream of threatening a man who has lost possession of his wits."

"If only you had let me know – I might have borrowed some from your vast store."

"I tell you, it never does one any harm to listen to both sides of a question."

"So that's your final word, is it? Well, then, I swear by Olympus you will not go unpunished. Bring the wretched girl here this very instant! She will die before his eyes."

"Do not imagine I will stay to watch. You will never see my face again. Perhaps then you will stop ranting at all who have the patience to bear with you."

With these words, Haemon turned on his heel and stormed out in angry grief.

"He ran off with a wild look in his eye, your majesty," the leader of the elders said. "He is beside himself, and I fear he may do something rash."

"Whatever he does, he will not get those two off."

"Do you mean to kill both maidens, then?"

"No, I am not unreasonable, but she who did the burying will be buried herself."

"Have you decided, then, what death she is to suffer?"

"I shall have her shut up in a deep cave, but I will leave a little food, so her death cannot be blamed upon the city. When she is imprisoned there, let her beg Hades to take pity on her, for he's the only god she worships. Then she may understand, although too late, that it does not pay to honour the dead more highly than the living."

With these words, Creon went back into the palace, while the chorus of the elders, filled with pity for Antigone and Haemon, began to chant a hymn to the love which conquers all.

Love, you drive all before you.
Love, all things are yours.
You, who watch out the night
On the soft cheeks of maidens;
You, who race over the seas
And are present in humble cabins,
Neither immortal god
Nor mortal man can escape you,
And the moment you have triumphed
He loses his will for ever.

You drive the just to injustice.
You kindled that hatred between them.
But love for the maiden has triumphed,
The great Aphrodite's victorious
And each man must follow his nature.

Alas! They are bringing the maiden.
Antigone walks to her death
And we, to whom tears are forbidden,
Feel the warm, bitter flow on our cheeks.

"Citizens!" cries the maiden,
"The dark road which I now tread
Leads on to my new inheritance,

My last farewell to the sun.
Faithful to my great duty,
A bride who was never wed,
I go forward to meet Hades
And share his marriage-bed."

"In honour you go, noble maiden.
No sickness has faded your cheeks,
No cruel sword wounded your flesh,
Yet you suffer beyond all bearing
As they lead you down death's pathway
To pay for your parents' sins."

"Black fate of my generation!
Dear father, O mother sweet,
Who bore me in sinful wedlock,
I come, I come to you now;
And to you, brother, who called me
To be at your side in death
I hasten, to join you who love me.
See, Creon the king has arrived!
And the end is drawing near."

"You will gain nothing by this miserable wailing!" Creon
cried. "Take her away, guards, and shut her up in the place I

... "Take her away, guards"...

ordered. If she dies there, it will be no fault of ours. She is not
fit to live among us."

> *"O tomb, my bridal chamber,*
> *My home buried deep in the earth,*
> *The gateway which leads me to Hades*
> *– So many I love are there!*
> *Yet I make my descent heavy-hearted,*
> *Before I hear wedding songs*
> *Or the sweet cries of my own child.*
>
> *Mortals have found me guilty*
> *Of tending my brother's corpse.*
> *If that be a crime I committed,*
> *The judges of Hades will say;*
> *But if they have done me injustice,*
> *May they suffer no worse than I."*

"Why must we put up with this?" roared Creon. "Take her
away before you start crying, too!"

> *"Alas! my fate overtakes me!*
> *O, gods of our fathers, see!*
> *And you, O Theban elders,*
> *What end is decreed, and by whom,*

For the princess who honoured her kin."

"Enough!" yelled Creon, beside himself with rage. Then the guards caught hold of Antigone, while once again the elders spoke.

Such was the lot of unhappy Danae:
Shut in a bronze chest like a tomb,
She exchanged the light of day for the dark.
Though of noble blood, there was no escape
For all that she bore Zeus' son in her womb.
Destiny's power is mighty indeed
And neither through wealth nor by force of arms,
Cyclopean walls or the stoutest of ships
Has anyone ever escaped her grasp.

"But look," broke off an elder, "here comes a boy leading Teiresias, the blind seer who knows all things."

"What news do you bring us, Teiresias?" Creon enquired.

"I will explain. Just hear me out attentively, and in good faith."

"I have always relied on your advice, wise elder."

"That is why you hold the reins of power in this land."

"You have helped me greatly, as I have always said."

"But now, Creon you are walking on the razor's edge."

"This is disturbing news indeed. Explain yourself."

"You will understand if I tell you the signs I have received. I was sitting on the throne from which I draw my visionary powers by listening to the birds' prophetic cries, when angry screeches and a wild beating of wings came to my ears, as if a flock of crows were furiously tearing at something with their claws. I was afraid and asked my boy here to tell me what signs a burnt offering would reveal. Terrible things happened then – the fire would give no flame, the fat ran from the thigh bones and they burst open, hurling gobbets of flesh into the air. The spleens were scattered and the meat curled upwards, revealing the bare bone beneath. Now I learn that the same signs have been repeated right across the city, that its hearths and altars have been choked with the flesh of the unlucky son of Oedipus, who was devoured by the vultures and the jackals. The gods will no longer accept our prayers or our sacrifices, no flame rises from the altars but only smoke, and the birds utter cries I cannot understand. Yet the explanation is simple: they have tasted the flesh and blood of an unburied man. You must decide what's to be done, my lord. Mistakes are only human, but they must be righted before it is too late. Obstinacy is a poor counsellor. Do not persist in striking at the dead. It is no way to prove your power, nor will heeding wise advice diminish you in any way."

"Old man, it seems that all of you, like archers, have chosen me as your target. This is not the first time a seer has turned his weapons on me. I know you all too well, you and your like. You are nothing more than tradesmen! Electrum from Sardis, gold from the Indies, whatever puts wealth in your coffers, you bring it here for sale. But for all that, you could not bury him! I do not care whether the eagles of almighty Zeus carry his torn flesh up to Olympus, or even if they befoul his throne with it, for I know the gods cannot be defiled by such things. So, Teiresias, let me tell you this: evil men come to an evil end when they cloak their cunning in fair words to line their pockets."

"Creon, I have nothing to say to you but this: do you know what our most precious possession is?"

"You are the man of wisdom here, so why not tell us?"

"Reason, your majesty."

"Just as folly is a man's most worthless quality."

"And you, unfortunately, have more than your share of that."

"If you were not a seer, I would give you the answer you deserve."

"Haven't you already done so?"

"Then I did well. All you soothsayers ply your trade for money."

"Yes, we just follow the example of our noble rulers."

"Do not forget who you are talking to!"

"Not for a moment – but neither do I forget that it was thanks to me you saved this city."

"You may be a wise seer, but you are cunning as a fox."

"Go on like this, and you will force me to reveal matters which should not be spoken of."

"Tell all – but do not imagine you will profit by it."

"Very well! Then know that before the sun has journeyed many times around the world you will pay for your wicked stubbornness by losing someone very close to you. For by closing a living soul inside her grave and leaving unburied a dead man who belongs to the gods of the nether world, you have been guilty of the most wicked and impious of deeds. Why, the gods of Olympus have no right to do such a thing, let alone you, a mere mortal. Be ready for the Erinnyes, for they will come to heap misfortunes on you like those that you have brought on others. Search all you will if you think I tell you this to gain some profit by it. Creon, the time is drawing near when you will hear wails of lamentation in your house fit only for the likes of those who leave the dogs, the wild beasts and the vultures to carry out the duties which are owed the dead. Arrows, you spoke of? Then I have shot my quiver-full, but god knows, you gave me enough provocation. Now you are wounded to the heart, great Creon, and there is no escape for you. Come, boy, take me home and let us leave this man to vent his wrath on younger heads. Yet in the end he will learn the need for self-control and reason."

"Your majesty, the seer has left, but we are terrified by what he said. In all our many years, we have never known him tell a lie."

"I know it all too well, and I am deeply troubled. I have gone in too far to withdraw and yet I fear some great disaster will now crush my pride."

"Son of Menoeceus, this is a time for cautious thinking."

"Then tell me what to do and I shall follow your advice."

"Run to save the maiden from the tomb where you shut her up alive, and give the luckless corpse a proper burial."

"So you think it right that I should go back on my word?"

"Indeed I do – before the wrath of Zeus descends upon you."

"Alas, it seems I have no choice. I must do as you say."

"And do it as quickly as you can, for the swift Erinnyes have wings upon their feet."

"How hard it is for me to go back on my decision, but circumstances drive me to it."

"Then hurry! And go yourself. Do not leave the task to others."

"Come, men! Bring picks and follow me to the cave. It was I who walled her up and I must be the one who sets her free. It is no more than my duty. I should have shown more piety and respect for the gods' unwritten laws."

With these words, Creon led his retainers off while the
chorus broke into song:

> *O son of Almighty Zeus,*
> *Strong shoot of Cadmus's daughter,*
> *Iacchus, Bacchus, Dionysus*
> *And whatever of many names*
> *Mortals and gods may call you;*
> *You who rule over Eleusis,*
> *Italia's renowned protector,*
> *You who are Thebes' great pride,*
> *Her god and her royal master;*
> *Who leads the Maenads in dance:*
> *Now by Ismenus' waters,*
> *Now by the Castalian spring*
> *Beneath the twin peaks of Parnassus,*
> *And now in these fields of Thebes*
> *Where the dragon's teeth were scattered;*
> *To you, our god, we fall down*
> *In humble supplication,*
> *O Bacchus Dionysus;*
> *Begging you come to the aid*
> *Of glorious Thebes, your city,*
> *Now fallen on evil days.*
> *Come, master, do not delay!*

> *Come, and bring us salvation.*

The elders had just ended their chant when a messenger came running with a troubled face and told them:

"You, descendants of old Cadmus and children of renowned Amphion, hear what I have to say: nothing is certain in this world of men. Chance rules us as she will. One moment she raises a man high and the next she casts him into deep misfortune. Who would have guessed what Creon's fate would be, he who enjoyed great fame and wealth, and the delights of home and children? Yet hear how he is fallen. For when a man loses all that gives him joy, he is no better than the living dead. There is no wealth or royal power in this world I would exchange for happiness."

"This prologue of yours bodes ill, I fear. Come, tell us quickly: what tragedy has struck the king?"

"Death has entered his house."

"Who is dead, and how? Don't keep us in suspense."

"Haemon has killed himself."

"Why? Tell us all."

"When he saw Antigone lying dead, it was more than he could bear."

"O seer, how truly you have spoken! But look, here comes queen Eurydice. Can she have heard about her son?"

"Citizens of unhappy Thebes, I have. When I heard the

dreadful news I lost my senses and sank into my ladies' arms. But I mustered up my courage and came out, for I am no stranger to misfortune and I must learn the whole sad story."

"Then I shall tell you, mistress, for I was there. I shall hide nothing from you. For there is no comfort to be had in words which soon prove false. I was with those who went to show your husband where Polyneices' corpse was lying. When we reached the spot, we begged Pluto and Hecate to restrain their wrath at the dead man's lying unburied and torn at by the dogs. Then we washed the body with fresh water and burnt the poor remains on a pyre of green branches. Finally, we raised a funeral mound over the ashes. Having covered Polyneices with the soil of his native land, we set off for the hollow cave, the bridal chamber of Charon and the maiden. As we approached, a soldier who had been keeping watch ran up and told Creon he had heard cries of grief coming from inside. The king drew near with anxious steps and then, from deep within the cave we heard broken cries of sorrow mixed with confused words. Suddenly Creon let out a loud groan and began to beat his breast in misery. 'That was my son's voice!' he cried out. 'Run, slaves, and search among the rocks, to see if Haemon is there or if the gods are mocking me.' When we reached the spot, we found the stones that blocked the entrance pushed aside and an awful spectacle within: the girl was hanging lifeless by a cord made from the torn strips of her veil and your son was clutching her around the waist and weeping, all the while breaking into curses at his father, who had caused her frightful death. The moment Creon saw him, he cried out, 'What are you doing here, unhappy boy? Do not do anything foolish. Come out, my son! On bended knee I beg you.' Instead of answering, Haemon spat in his father's face, then drew his sword and rushed upon him. Creon sprang to one side to escape the thrust, at which Haemon drove the blade with all his strength between his own ribs. As the life drained from him, the poor boy clasped the maiden and supported himself upon her hanging body, until at last his passionate grasp weakened and he sank dead at her dangling feet. And that is how Haemon married Antigone in the bridal chamber of Hades. May his madness be a lesson to us all."

Eurydice had heard the terrible story out in silence. But when the tale was told, she turned on her heel and rushed back into the palace. The elders were taken by surprise and their leader said:

"I do not know how to account for this silence of the queen's, but I can say this: it frightens me."

"I cannot explain it, either," said the messenger, "but perhaps she wishes to be free to cry alone, instead of mourning for her son out here, in front of all of us. Whatever it is, I suppose that she must have her reasons, for she is no fool."

"And yet her stony silence troubles me far more than any

pointless show of grief. But here comes the king. In his eyes you can read all the agony of this disaster he has brought upon himself."

"Alas!" cried Creon when he reached them. "My guilt is horrible! My hands are stained with my own blood! Ah, luckless boy, my obstinacy killed you. You are gone in the flower of your youth, my pride and joy, my own dear son!"

"Unhappy man! Why did you take so long to see the course you should have taken?"

"Some god, alas, who envied me my happiness, darkened my mind and drove me to rash deeds. How intolerable the sufferings of mortals are!"

"King!" cried a guard, who now came rushing from the palace. "Add new sorrows to those you are suffering already!"

"No! No, I beg you! This house has had its fill of horrors."

"The queen has killed herself."

"Oh, no! It is not possible! Why, Zeus? why?"

"Because your son's death was more than she could bear."

"Ah, Hades! How you rend my heart! Do you seek to kill a man who is already dead? Yet maybe I did not hear the soldier well. What did you say, lad? Is it true?"

"See for yourself. Here they come, bringing out the queen's body."

"The blows fall thick and fast, and I cannot withstand them. But moments past I clutched my dead son in my arms – and

... "When a man suffers and pays for his deeds
He will see reason: alas, too late"...

now I see my poor wife's body lying here. How did you take your life, my darling?"

"She took a dagger and stabbed herself, after heaping curses on the murderer of her son – on you, the author of all your family's miseries."

"Alas, and she was right. I, and I alone, am guilty. There is no one else on whom I can lay any blame, neither god nor mortal. I killed you, son; I killed that splendid maiden and I killed your mother, too, miserable creature that I am! Take me and drive me far away, for all is lost with Creon."

"That would be the only good course left to you – if we can speak of good amid so many evils," said the leader of the elders. "It would be far worse for you to go on living among the graves which you yourself have opened."

"I would rather not live at all. Let death come in its vilest shape and put an ending to my life. My eyes must never look upon the light of day again. Take me away, fool that I am. In my blindness I have brought death on those I loved and the most hideous of misfortunes on myself."

"O reason!" cried the chorus,

> *O, reason!*
> *You alone can bring happiness.*
> *The unwritten laws demand respect;*
> *The immortal gods ask our piety.*

Ah, folly!
With your obstinacy and your impious words
You open wounds too deep to be healed.
When a man suffers and pays for his deeds
He will see reason: alas, too late.

THE EPIGONI

When the priest of Athena drew the sacred furrow with his plough around the base of the Acropolis, he always spoke these words:

"Never refuse a stranger water or the warmth of a fire. Never point out any way but the right one. Deny no man a grave. Never kill the ox which draws the plough."

And indeed, the dead were always given the burial rites which custom had laid down. For if the body was allowed to lie unburied and unmourned, the soul would suffer eternal anguish. None were punished in the Underworld but Sisyphus,

Tantalus, Ixion and the forty-nine Danaids. Nobody else paid for his earthly crimes in Hades, whether he had been king or common soldier, enemy or friend, just or unjust. 'The dead deserve their peace', the saying went, and there were no distinctions made in that dark kingdom. All that was first required was that the dead be given the honours that were due to them.

Thus we see that after nearly every battle a truce would be declared, so that each side could gather up its dead and perform the funeral rites. But when hatred and the thirst for vengeance knew no bounds, then the opposite would happen: new fighting would break out around some corpse as the dead warrior's comrades tried to take him off and bury him while his enemies fought to snatch him from their hands and gain revenge by making his soul suffer through all eternity.

That is why Antigone sacrificed herself to sprinkle earth on her dead brother, while Creon, driven by revengeful fury, commanded that he lie unburied.

Although a tomb was finally raised for Polyneices, the anger of the gods did not cease to plague unhappy Thebes – for all the Argive dead were left unburied, too.

Thus, when news of the disaster came to Argos, and it was learned that the corpses of their soldiers were still lying on the Theban plain, in a storm of angry grief the wives and mothers of the seven leaders took their children and went to

Athens to seek the support of king Theseus.

Theseus heard them out with sympathy, but while he was pondering what steps to take, a message came from Creon demanding he expel the Argive wives and mothers from his city. Thus soon had the headstrong Creon forgotten the disaster which had struck when he left Polyneices to be eaten by the birds of prey. Now here he was, asking for more trouble. Trouble was precisely what he got: Theseus was so enraged by the Theban's impiety and insolence that he immediately attacked his city.

In the battle which took place outside the walls, Creon was defeated and the men of Thebes were obliged to withdraw and seek the protection of their ramparts, leaving their dead in the hands of the Athenians. The victors, who sought no further gains, piled up the Argive corpses, which still lay where they had fallen, and, lighting seven huge fires, burned all the dead of the earlier battle with the honours the Thebans had denied them. But their leaders they took to Eleusis, to be buried where their wives were waiting for the bodies.

When these had been placed upon the pyre, the dead chiefs' sons stepped forward. Though but children, on seeing how their fathers had been chewed and pecked at by the dogs and crows, they swore a solemn oath. "May we die landless and without a tomb to cover us," they cried, "and may our souls suffer endless torments if we do not return to seek our venge-

ance and raze Thebes to the ground!" The words the young-
sters swore that day boded new ills for that unlucky city.

With heavy hearts, the wives and children of the heroes
brought their ashes back to Argos. One of them did not return. This was Evadne, the wife of Capaneus, whose body
was considered sacred because he had been killed by Zeus
himself. For this reason he had been buried separately, with
all the honours due to a glorious hero. But when his funeral
pyre was lit, and the hungry flames were licking at the corpse,
Evadne, unable to bear her husband's death, threw herself
into the fire and was burnt along with him.

Neither was the wise Amphiaraus among those who were
honoured at Eleusis on that day. For as he had fled, with a
Theban about to strike him down, Zeus had opened up the
earth and the great seer had disappeared together with his
chariot. On the same spot, the Athenians later built a sanctu-
ary for healing and divination, where they worshipped Amphiaraus as a god. Its remains can still be seen today.

Ten years went by, and the boys who had sworn that solemn oath were now grown into hardened manhood. Trained
in the arts of war, they were ready to launch a new campaign
against the city of Thebes.

The Epigoni, as these young leaders were called, gathered
a far greater army at Argos than had set off on the earlier
expedition. They planned to install Thersander, the son of

Polyneices, as the new king of Thebes. Among the others, the following stood out: burly Diomedes, son of Tydeus, and his inseparable friend Sthenelus, whose father had been Capaneus. Then there was Aegialeus, the son of king Adrastus. The remaining leaders of the force were Promachus, Parthenopaeus's son; Polydorus, the son of Hippomedon and, in overall command, Alcmaeon, son of the seer Amphiaraus.

Yet Alcmaeon, whose father had been shielded by Zeus himself and thus not torn to pieces by the dogs and birds, had not been present when the oath was sworn, and was the only one who had no wish to take part in the war. He remembered the words his father had spoken to him on setting off for Thebes:

"My powers of vision tell me I shall not return from battle. When you grow to manhood, you must avenge my death. Yet it is not the Thebans who are guilty. It is your mother, who forced me to go out and fight so she could have the magic necklace of eternal youth which Aphrodite gave to Harmonia. She is the one from whom you must seek vengeance."

But this was not the only crime Alcmaeon's mother Eriphyle was guilty of. Now, as before, she was ready to move mountains to force her son to take part in the campaign; for the cunning Thersander had promised her Harmonia's veil as well, another miraculous gift, this time from Athena, on her marriage with king Cadmus.

Now Alcmaeon was torn between two loyalties. On the one hand, his ears rang with his father's last command, and on the other he felt obliged to meet his mother's wishes. Finally he sought the advice of the oracle at Delphi, to tell him where his duty lay. Apollo answered him as follows:

"You must obey them both. You are to bow to your mother's wishes and set off at the head of the Argive army, for only you are capable of bringing victory; but you must also be obedient to your father, since if you do not take revenge, his soul will suffer for all time."

Having received this reply, Alcmaeon had no choice but to lead the Argive army against Thebes. For counsellor he had king Adrastus, who again took part in the campaign. The troops set off at once, for all the auguries were good. The gods were with the Epigoni, and the city they were headed for was destined to pay for its old sins.

This time, the defender of Thebes was Laodamas, the son of Eteocles.

A hard but decisive battle was fought outside the walls. Aegialeus, son of Adrastus, led the first charge, cheered on by the Argives, and caused immediate confusion in the Theban ranks. But his advance was soon cut short when Laodamas himself stepped forth and killed him with a savage spear-thrust. He had no time to enjoy this victory, however, for a moment later he met death at Alcmaeon's sword. Now the Thebans were fighting without a leader and suffered such heavy losses that they were obliged to pull back and take refuge in the city.

Meanwhile, on the Argive side, Adrastus had died of grief on hearing of his son's death. When word of this reached Thebes it caused Teiresias grave concern, for the great seer had learned by his divining arts that the city would fall upon the death of the last of the Seven who had led the first campaign. The news was so ominous that he advised his fellow-citizens to flee their homes that very night and seek out a new homeland. And so the Thebans took their wives and children and what few belongings they could carry, and under cover of darkness they left the city to the enemy and began a long trek northwards.

Next morning the Argives poured through the undefended gates, and in a vengeful frenzy plundered and destroyed whatever lay before them. Then they loaded their spoils on waggons and returned to Argos, leaving Thersander to rule the poor remains of the once-proud city with its seven gates.

Among the few prisoners who fell into Argive hands was Manto, the daughter of Teiresias. Out of respect for the great soothsayer, they did not make the girl a slave, but dedicated her to Apollo, at his Oracle in Delphi. There Manto became his priestess, foretelling men's futures with mysterious, two-edged prophecies.

As for Teiresias himself, he left the city with the others

but, overcome with exhaustion, stopped at the spring of
Tilphussa to rest and drink. And there he died. Having wept
for this man who had helped three generations of his fellow-
citizens, the Thebans buried his body near the spring and then
went on their way. Some of them finally reached North
Euboea, where they founded the city of Istiaia, while others
headed north-west and found refuge in Illyria, where the city's
founder Cadmus and his wife Harmonia had once fled into
exile, and where their son Illyrius later reigned. In time, however, many of the Thebans returned to the city of their birth.

Meanwhile, in Argos, Alcmaeon found himself cast in a
hated role. He was fated to take vengeance on his mother, yet
how could he bring himself to commit so foul a deed? Although Eriphyle's vanity had cost his father's life and put his
own in danger, Alcmaeon was tormented by the thought that
he must kill the woman who had borne him, and knew that
once the deed was done he would never enjoy a moment's
peace. He had no choice, however. He was bound not merely
by his father's wish but by a god's command: that of Apollo
himself.

Thus an unwilling son killed his own mother and paid the
price that he had feared. Pursued by the Erinnyes and abandoned by his wife Arsinoe, Alcmaeon became a homeless
wanderer. Wherever he went, he found doors closed against
him, for who would help a man whose hands were stained

with his mother's blood? In the end, he went to Delphi to consult the oracle, hoping to learn if his sufferings might one day end.

"Only in a land where your crime is not yet known will you find refuge and salvation," was the answer he received.

Yet where could such a land be found? On and on he trudged until he reached the mighty river Achelous. Worn out, starving and in rags, he knelt upon its bank and told the river-god the whole sad story. Achelous was moved to pity, and rising from the waters he washed off the guilty stains of Eriphyle's blood and told Alcmaeon to go and live on an island in the river-mouth which had only recently been formed by silt the waters had brought down.

"Nobody will drive you from this island," said the god. "Your crime has never been heard of there, for when you committed it, it did not even exist."

So Alcmaeon at last found a place where he was safe, and there he married Achelous' daughter, the river-nymph Callirrhoe.

Thinking his troubles were over, he sat down and told his wife all that had happened, to take the load from off his mind.

But when Callirrhoe heard about Harmonia's veil and necklace, with their magic powers, she longed to have eternal youth herself, and demanded that Alcmaeon bring them to her.

"These gifts have brought nothing but disaster!" Alcmaeon

cried in horror. "One of them caused my father's death and made me kill my mother, and the other nearly proved the end of me. Because of them I have never known a moment's peace."

But Callirrhoe was not a woman who was easily put off.

"If you love me truly, you must bring them," she retorted. And she was so insistent that in the end Alcmaeon relented and went reluctantly to do her bidding.

Now the veil and the necklace were still in the hands of Arsinoe, his former wife, who had nursed a deadly hatred for him since the day when he had killed his mother. Even so, Alcmaeon managed to persuade her.

"I shall give them to you – but it will cost you dearly!" she warned him.

"I know," replied Alcmaeon. Yet he could not guess how dearly he would pay.

He set off with the gifts, but Callirrhoe never got them. For when he reached his home, Arsinoe's two brothers were lying in wait. Without a word, they drew their swords and felled him.

And so the unlucky son of Amphiaraus met his death. He had led the Epigoni to victory, but the gods had reserved the cruellest of fates for him.

Of his companions, Diomedes won great glory in the Trojan war, while Sthenelus and others fought with distinction there as well.

But these two wars, the Theban and the Trojan, marked the ending of an epoch, or, as Hesiod terms it, the end of 'the fourth generation of mankind', the renowned generation of the heroes. Indeed there is but little to tell before the mythical age draws to its final close. This is the story of a second group of 'Epigoni', the descendants of the hero Heracles, or the 'Heraclids' as they were called. Their legendary return marks the end of Greek mythology.

To trace this story to its origins, we must go back to a time shortly after Heracles' death, when his tormentor, the vain and cowardly Eurystheus, still held the throne of Mycenae.

In the neighbouring city of Tiryns, Heracles' son Hyllus was living with his mother Alcmene and several of his brothers. Eurystheus was as terrified of them as he had been of their father. "When Heracles' children grow to manhood, they will seek revenge," he told himself, and decided to banish them beyond the frontiers of his kingdom. That was not all he did. He knew that Heracles had many other sons in various cities. If they united they would surely prove strong enough to threaten both his kingdom and his life – and so he asked the other kings of Greece to act as he had done and cast them out. In those days the ruler of Mycenae was known as the Great King, and thus his orders were obeyed by all the other monarchs – except Theseus of Athens, who welcomed all of

Heracles' children and gave them shelter at nearby Marathon. Thus Eurystheus achieved the very opposite of what he had intended: instead of the Heraclids being scattered safely beyond the Greek frontiers, they were now all gathered in one place. From then on, Eurystheus lived in constant fear; and as the children grew, so did his anxiety. In the end, he decided that the matter could only be resolved by war.

By now Theseus' son Demophon was king of Athens, and he decided to support the Heraclids. Not that they were quite defenceless: Hyllus, their leader, was a fearless lad, and Iolaus, the hero's nephew, had come to the young men's aid with a strong band of warriors. Iolaus had often helped Heracles when Eurystheus was trying to destroy him and now, though elderly, was intent on one thing only: revenge.

However, the Heraclids faced a cruel difficulty: an oracle had promised victory but only if one of Heracles' children were sacrificed before the battle. The young men had decided to draw lots, when his daughter, young Macaria, came forward of her own accord and offered up the flower of her youth that her brothers might be saved.

Then, helped by the Athenians, the Heraclids won a crushing victory and routed the forces of Eurystheus. Their cowardly leader fled in his chariot, whipping the horses frenziedly in his panic-stricken flight. Iolaus saw him go, and remembering all the suffering and danger that Heracles had undergone on Eurystheus' account, he begged great Zeus to give him back for just one day his youth and former strength.

Zeus granted him this favour, and suddenly Iolaus' old, bent body straightened and bloomed as he stood there in his chariot. He was transformed once more into the handsome, strong young man who had once helped Heracles perform his labours. He launched his horses into a thundering gallop, caught up with Eurystheus in a flash, and drawing back one muscular, bronzed arm he launched a javelin with such terrible force that it hurled Eurystheus from his chariot and pinned him dead upon the ground.

Such was the end of the 'Great King' of Mycenae, who died as he had lived, in panic-stricken fear. Yet for all his crimes against Heracles and his children, Eurystheus was not denied a grave. The victors set aside a plot of land and raised a funeral mound above him at Pallini, mid-way between Marathon and Athens.

The Heraclids now went to live as guests in Thebes, but they soon began to feel they lacked a homeland. Determined to depend on hospitality no more, and confident that they now had the strength to beat down all resistance, they decided to go back to the Peloponnese and settle in the only part of Greece they could truly call their own.

Led by Hyllus, they crossed the Isthmus and defeated the Argive forces. But sickness and famine then swept the land

and the Heraclids were plunged into despair. They asked the oracle at Delphi what was to blame for their misfortunes and were told they had not come back at the right time. They must 'wait for the third crop', the priestess said.

Taking this to mean 'the third year', they withdrew once more to Marathon and patiently counted off the seasons before setting out for the Peloponnese once again. Another Argive army met them at the Isthmus, this time led by Atreus, the new king of Mycenae.

Again, things turned out badly for the Heraclids. When the two armies were drawn up for battle, Hyllus, who wished to avoid an unnecessary blood-bath, stepped forward and cried:

"I call upon the bravest man among you to fight with me in single combat. If he wins, the Heraclids will leave and not come back until a hundred years have passed; but if I succeed in killing him, you will hand over the whole of the Peloponnese to us."

Then the fearless Echemus sprang forward. He was king of Tegea, and a spearsman of such speed and power that he had never been defeated. Hyllus was no coward, but he was outmatched both in skill and strength, and moments later he lay dead at Echemus's feet.

Numb with grief, the Heraclids took up their dead leader and withdrew. They made camp at Megara while they gave Hyllus a proper burial and considered where they could go next. There seemed no choice but to return once more to Marathon – but how much longer could the Athenians go on offering them such refuge? Soon after, they decided to launch a third campaign against the Peloponnese. Again it was a failure, and again they were faced by the same problem. It was enough to make them weep. Here they were, the sons and grandsons of the greatest hero Greece had ever known, and yet they did not have a single corner of the land to call their own. At last they thought of Doris, where Heracles had once owned some estates, and they set off on the long march west to claim their ancient birthright. Fortunately, the people of the region welcomed the Heraclids with open arms. "Better to make a good friend and an ally than face yet another enemy," they told themselves. This wise decision was to stand them in good stead.

Despite the welcome they received in Doris, the Heraclids could not forget their repeated disappointments further south. They felt bitter because the oracle which had promised them the Peloponnese at 'the third crop' had not proved true, and so they went again to Delphi to seek an explanation.

"It is not the oracle which is to blame," the priests of Apollo told them, "but you, who did not read its meaning properly. 'Third crop' did not mean 'third harvest of the land' but 'the third generation of men' – Heracles' great-grandsons."

So the Heraclids decided to wait until the time was ripe.

Meanwhile, they multiplied and grew in strength. And since for three generations they had lived and married among the Dorians, in time they came to be indistinguishable from the local people.

This brings us to the time which followed the Theban and the Trojan wars. The Heraclids of the third generation were now impatient for the long-awaited 'return'. With them would go a mighty Dorian army, equally ready for the descent upon the Peloponnese. However, the combined forces were under the command of Heraclids alone: the brothers Temenus and Cresphontes and the twins Procles and Eurysthenes.

In those days, Mycenae was ruled by Tisamenus, son of Orestes and grandson of Agamemnon. He had married Hermione, the daughter of Menelaus and the lovely Helen, thus effecting a union between his own kingdom and bordering Sparta which made him confident of his superior power.

Not that this troubled the Heraclids and their Dorian allies. They had been preparing for this war for years and no Tisamenus was about to stop them. They set off on their campaign confident of victory. This time, they avoided the route which would lead them through the Isthmus, and where three times their forebears had known failure. Instead, they chose to cross into the Peloponnese from Naupactus, where they had a great fleet lying at anchor. There their numbers were swelled by yet more reinforcements when they were joined by the Aetolians, who had always cast a hungry eye upon the opposite shore.

Before they set sail, they sought the advice of the oracle at Delphi, a step always taken before great undertakings in those days.

"All will go well with you if you have Triops as your guide," the oracle announced.

Now consternation reigned, for there was not a man in all the army who had ever heard the name.

Finally, somebody recalled that he had heard of such a person, but far away across the eastern sea, on the distant island of Rhodes.

"Then we must send for him," a voice called out.

"Rhodes is a very long voyage from here," Temenus reminded them, "and none of us knows whether it will be possible to bring him, or if so, when. All that can come of this is that the Argives will be given time to make their preparations."

"If we ignore Apollo's counsels, we are lost!" cried many of the men.

"We shall be lost if we lose the advantage of surprise," retorted Temenus. "Fear not. I shall find a 'Triops' for you, without going very far."

Then he searched the camp, until he caught sight of the Aetolian chief Oxylus, who was riding a one-eyed horse.

Going up to him, he asked,

"Have you ever been across to the Peloponnese?"

"Why, I know it like the back of my hand. I spent years in exile there."

"I have found the man we're looking for!" Temenus announced. "We all know what 'Triops' means: 'he who has three eyes'. There you are, just look: two on the man and one more on the horse! Prepare to board at once! We're crossing over!"

With cries of joy, the army eagerly embarked.

Temenus' surprise attack achieved its aim. One by one the cities of the Peloponnese fell to the Heraclids' assault. Tisamenus put up a valiant but vain resistance. His only achievement was to go down in history as the last of all the Atreids. The deciding battle was fought on the plain of Lerna, where Tisamenus was killed, his army scattered and the rule of the invaders established beyond all further question.

After their victory, the Heraclids and their Dorian allies parcelled out the Peloponnese among them, with the exception of Achaia, which was granted to Oxylus. Lots were cast to establish who would get which share. The lot marked with a toad stood for Mycenae, and it fell to Temenus; the one which had a fox engraved upon it represented Messene, and it went to Cresphontes, while the one which had a serpent on it stood for Sparta and went to the twins Procles and

... And there, mythology draws to its mysterious close...

Eurysthenes, which is why Sparta was for ever after ruled by two kings.

The 'return of the Heraclids' had been achieved, and with it the 'descent of the Dorians'. And there, mythology draws to its mysterious close. It tells of only one more king in Mycenae, Deiphontes, who ascended the throne of Temenus on marrying his daughter Hyrnitho.

And afterwards?

Afterwards, quite abruptly, a thick black curtain descends upon Greek mythology. The mythical years end with a tragic suddenness. Mycenaean civilization quite literally disappears, and all the cities of Greece are destroyed or sink into utter insignificance. And there is not a single myth or tale to tell us how this happened. Only the names of the last rulers of Mycenae are left to us: Deiphontes and Hyrnitho, two players in a tragedy whose text has never been discovered. Three centuries of silence follow, a long, blank period which have been quite rightly termed 'The Dark Ages of Greece'.

But while the lights had gone out and a glorious civilization been ground into the dust, while the voices which sang of new achievements had been silenced and no new myths would ever be created, the voices which recounted glories past could not be stilled. From mouth to mouth, mythology was passed on, surviving the storm which swept all else before it, a tiny light of song in a darkness which dragged out for twenty generations, to be delivered safe at last into worthy, strong new hands. The first and greatest of them all was Homer, who reshaped the brilliant raw material to make it more brilliant still. And when at last Athens came into the bright light of day in which Mycenae had once basked, Aeschylus, Sophocles and Euripides did not have far to seek for the themes of their immortal tragedies. They were there in abundance, in Greek mythology, and audiences which paid due honour to the good and lovely clamoured for them. Was it surprising, when every citizen of Athens from six to eighteen years of age received an education which included a firm grounding in the arts? How then could mediocrity pass unchallenged, and theatres playing masterpieces not be filled?

Nor should we forget that the three hundred thousand citizens of Athens were not alone in adoring poetry and great art. At the height of the Athenian democracy, her influence spread throughout the Aegean and Asia Minor, to Sicily, southern Italy and even the Mediterranean shores of France and Spain. In all these places theatres were built and filled with people who had been nourished from the same inexhaustible source of values: Greek mythology, an inheritance which has been passed on from generation to generation, century to century, millennium to millennium, and, overcoming countless obstacles, has survived into our own troubled age without losing any of its power or radiance.

A BOY AND HIS DREAM

How much of history lies hidden in mythology? A considerable amount – very considerable, we might say, if we include in our definition of the word the customs, knowledge and beliefs of the people of distant times, which mythology tells us of so vividly.

However, the history which myth conceals is very different from the kind we are accustomed to: different because it was written, or rather shaped, in an age when, while there were no historians as such, there were hosts of poets and singers. As a result, this first, archaic history is unique in its freshness and imaginative qualities. For us today, mythology is not simply a source of knowledge, but a body of work which addresses itself to the mind and to the heart of modern man: to the mind because it spurs one to interpret and seek further, and to the heart because it strikes a chord of joyous recognition of human values that time has not erased nor frontiers halted.

Yet for all this, the days are not long past when archaeologists denied the historical element of myth and refused to see a single grain of truth in anything it told them. Then, one day, in a small town in Germany, a little boy of eight was given a book about the Trojan war. He devoured its pages eagerly, and gazed in fascination at a picture which showed the city of Troy in flames. Seeing their son's enthusiasm for the subject, his parents gave him Homer's Iliad as well. What he read there stirred his blood, and he pressed his father for more details. All he got for an answer was that these were splendid tales but nothing more.

"No!" cried the boy. "This war really happened!"

"There is no way we can tell," replied his father. "You see, this Troy the poem speaks of has never been found."

"It happened! It happened!" the boy insisted, "and when I grow up I will go in search of Troy. I'll dig until I find the ashes of the buried city, and I'll prove the war took place!" Bold word indeed, but they were only spoken by an eight-year-old, and nobody could have dreamed of taking them with the seriousness which they deserved.

It was not long before the boy lost both his parents and was forced to make a living for himself. Often he had no money to buy bread, but he always had enough for books and candles, and he would go on reading deep into the night when his long day's work was over. He learned foreign languages, read history and made a study of mythology. As for Homer, he learned all the poet's work by heart in the original, and he would often sit until the small hours reciting the Iliad aloud, carried away by the sweet cadences of the ancient language, warmed by its wealth of feeling, and living again, spellbound, its roar of battle and events which shook the world.

Forty years went by, and the boy had now become a prosperous merchant. Little by little, the pursuit of wealth had quenched his burning ardour to find Troy. Yet something of that fire still burned, like glowing coal among the ashes of his boyhood dream. Then, one day, on a business trip to London, he visited the British Museum and saw the marble panels which Lord Elgin had taken from the temple of the Parthenon in Athens. The mere sight of them was enough to rekindle his old hopes of finding the lost city. The matchless beauty of Pheidias' sculptures worked its enduring magic on the merchant, and once again the Homeric verses came thundering like a torrent through his mind, bringing to life before his very eyes the gods and heroes who had fought beneath the walls of Troy. The rich man in his early fifties became once more the boy fired by a noble vision. It was then he took his great decision. He gave up all his business ventures, divorced his wife, who called him mad and tried to stop him, and threw himself into a feverish study of archaeology. Soon after this, he set out at his own expense to fulfil the promise he had made himself more than forty years before.

Using the works of Homer as his guide, he soon located the site of ancient Troy, and in 1872, after two years of digging, he had brought to light not only the city's walls and the ashes of its burning, but a fabulous treasure of eight thousand gold and silver jewels and vessels. He then moved westwards over the Aegean to Mycenae and Orchomenus, where his work was crowned with the same brilliant success, and yet further west to Ithaca, in the Ionian sea, where he discovered Cyclopean walls. His name was Heinrich Schliemann, and his tireless companion and supporter throughout the long, hard years of excavation was his second wife, Sophia, a Greek.

With Schliemann's discoveries, the stubborn old theories were overthrown once and for all. Now it was clear that mythology was not mere tales, but had a solid foundation in historical events.

Then did the names of Achilles, Hector, Heracles, Jason, Theseus, Oedipus and so many other heroes of Greek myth belong to real people? Most certainly they did. Just as the names of all the most important cities mentioned in mythology have been found to correspond to real places, so the names of its greatest kings and heroes and the most likely of the events which it recounts have both proved true.

True to a point, that is. There is much that can never have corresponded to reality, being beyond the powers of man, and such elements can easily be distinguished. Yet there are many facets of mythology which deserve our careful thought and study. This need not be a field reserved for specialists: any reader can do what that small boy once did. Indeed, it would hardly be far-fetched to compare mythology to a fine work of modern art which draws us by its play of colours, its bold brush-strokes and its pleasing overall effect, but which we appreciate all the more if we can fathom what it represents. The same is true of myths, which, handed on by word of mouth from poet to poet and from bard to bard, became embroidered with such gorgeous colours that their radiance dulled the facts that lay beneath and made them seem mere fanciful tales, when at their heart they were not fairy-tales at all. Indeed, they were the very life and history of their times, yet rendered more to harmonize with the chords of the lyre which accompanied them than with strict regard for fact. Yet it was precisely because these stories told of life itself that they are true to life. In them, we will not find the improbable 'happy endings' which are the mark of fairy-tales. There are no such happy endings in mythology, or if there are, they are as rare as they were in the life of those hard times when cruel dramas were played out in palaces and tragedies written on the fields of battle.

GREEK MYTHOLOGY SERIES

AN INDEX OF ALL NAMES
appearing in this Greek Mythology series
is included in volume 4. Theseus - Perseus